Assessment Program B

VISIONS

Language ✧ Literature ✧ Content

Mary Lou McCloskey

Lydia Stack

THOMSON

HEINLE

Australia ✧ Canada ✧ Mexico ✧ Singapore ✧ United Kingdom ✧ United States

THOMSON

™

HEINLE

VISIONS ASSESSMENT PROGRAM B
Mary Lou McCloskey and Lydia Stack

Publisher: *Phyllis Dobbins*
Director of Development: *Anita Raducanu*
Developmental Editor: *Tania Maundrell-Brown*
Associate Developmental Editor: *Yeny Kim*
Associate Developmental Editor: *Kasia Zagorski*
Editorial Assistant: *Audra Longert*
Production Supervisor: *Mike Burggren*
Marketing Manager: *Jim McDonough*
Manufacturing Manager: *Marcia Locke*
Director, ELL Training and Development: *Evelyn Nelson*
Photography Manager: *Sheri Blaney*
Development: *Proof Positive/Farrowlyne Associates, Inc.*
Design and Production: *Proof Positive/Farrowlyne Associates, Inc.*
Cover Designer: *Studio Montage*
Printer: *Globus Printing Company*

Printed in the United States of America.
1 2 3 4 5 6 7 8 9 10   08 07 06 05 04 03

For more information, contact Heinle, 25 Thomson Place, Boston, Massachusetts 02210 USA, or you can visit our Internet site at http://www.heinle.com

For permission to use material from this text or product contact us:
Tel   1-800-730-2214
Fax   1-800-730-2215
Web www.thomsonrights.com

ISBN: 0-8384-5341-4

Contents

STUDENT TESTS

Introduction and Overview

The *Visions* Assessment Program was designed to ensure standards-based accountability for teachers and students alike. It begins with a Diagnostic Test to assess what students already know and to target students' needs in specific skill areas. Throughout the book, students take a Chapter Quiz at the end of each chapter. At the end of each unit, they take a Unit Test. The Assessment Program ensures ongoing as well as summative evaluation with the Mid-Book and End-of-Book Exams. Portfolio Assessment is also taken into account to measure the students' overall progress.

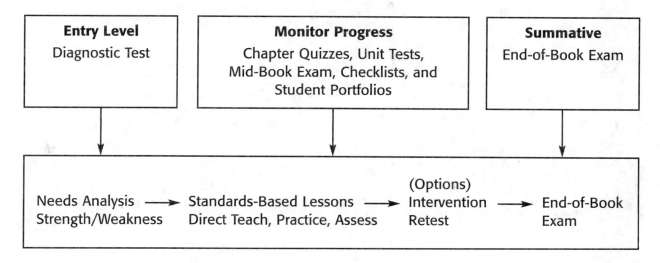

ExamView® is a CD-ROM assessment instrument that allows teachers to create and customize their *Visions* Assessment Program. The Chapter Quizzes, Unit Tests, Mid-Book Exam, and End-of-Book Exam can be customized by adding, deleting, editing, or rearranging questions from the test bank of standards-based assessment items. *ExamView*® also allows teachers to create and/or customize tests for the purpose of retesting after intervention.

ENTRY LEVEL PLACEMENT

Heinle recognizes that English Language Learners usually take a placement test such as the *Language Assessment Scales* (LAS), the *California English Language Development Test* (CELDT), the *IDEA Proficiency Test* (IPT), or the Woodcock Muñoz. Heinle provides correlations to these placement tests so teachers know where to place students in the *Visions* program. Contact your local Heinle/Thomson Learning Sales Representative for more information about these correlations.

ASSESSMENT REFERENCE CHART

The reference chart below provides an overview of the assessment instruments, page numbers, and purpose of the assessment tools in the *Visions* Assessment Program.

	Name	Pages	Purpose of Assessment
Entry Level	**Diagnostic Test**	1–6	To enable teachers to ascertain their students' skills in vocabulary, reading, grammar, spelling, and writing, and to perform a Needs Analysis in order to target specific instructional needs.
Monitor Progress	**Chapter Quizzes**	7–96	To monitor students' ongoing progress in vocabulary, grammar, reading, and writing. There are 27 Chapter Quizzes.
	Unit Tests	17–102	To monitor students' ongoing progress toward meeting strategies and standards in vocabulary, grammar, reading, and writing at the end of each unit. There are 6 Unit Tests.
	Mid-Book Exam	55–60	To monitor students' ongoing progress toward meeting strategies and standards in vocabulary, grammar, reading, and writing as taught throughout the first three units of the book.
	Student Resources Checklists	115–133	To promote student responsibility in meeting the standards. Students self-assess their strengths and weaknesses for purposes of reteaching if necessary.
Summative	**End-of-Book Exam**	103–108	To measure students' achievement and mastery in meeting the standards in vocabulary, reading, and writing as taught throughout the book.
	Peer Editing Checklists	117–120	To collaboratively involve classmates in giving and gaining feedback on their progress toward meeting the standards in writing.
	Active Listening Checklist	124	To collaboratively involve classmates in giving and gaining feedback on their progress in the area of listening and speaking during oral presentations.
Monitor Progress	**Teacher Resources** Listening, Speaking, Reading, Writing, Viewing, and Content Area Checklists	134	To track ongoing progress of students in all domains of the standards, and to serve as a vehicle in planning instruction.
	Reading Fluency	116, 136	To check students' progress in learning to read silently and aloud with expression, and to adjust their reading rates according to the purpose of their reading.
	Rubrics	136–137	To evaluate students' overall performance using a fixed measurement scale and a list of criteria taken from formal and informal outcomes. These rubrics should be part of each student's permanent record.
	Portfolio Assessment	115	To involve students in self-reflection on their progress in meeting their learning goals. This ongoing assessment is a collection of student work that exhibits the student's best efforts and progress.
	***ExamView*® CD-ROM**	CD-ROM	To empower teachers to choose and customize test items to meet students' targeted needs; items chosen may be used to retest after intervention activities.

ENTRY LEVEL

DIAGNOSTIC TEST

The following subtests appear in the Diagnostic Test. These subtests may be taken all at once or at multiple diagnostic sessions.

A. **Vocabulary Meaning Subtest** This subtest assesses the learner's vocabulary and ability to derive meaning from context. The ability to comprehend and read contextually is an indispensable skill, just as successful contextual reading requires an adequate vocabulary.

B. **Word Study Subtest** This subtest assesses the learner's ability to recognize parts of words (such as suffixes, prefixes, and roots) and to sound out words. It also assesses the dictionary skills covered in each level of *Visions* that pertain to word analysis.

C. **Reading Comprehension Subtest** This subtest evaluates the learner's ability to answer questions about a silently-read passage. The learner's reading rate (fluency) may also be measured in addition to his/her understanding of the reading.

D. **Reading Strategies Subtest** This subtest assesses the successful use of various reading strategies presented in *Visions*.

E. **Grammar/Usage Subtest** This subtest evaluates skills that match the standards taken from the Grammar Focus section of *Visions*.

F. **Spelling Subtest** This subtest assesses the learner's spelling skills. It mirrors the spelling skills found in the Writing section of the *Visions* Activity Book.

G. **Writing Subtest** This subtest assesses the learner's writing skills. Skills from this section mirror the writing practice given in *Visions*. Learners are asked to write in sentences.

H. **Writing Conventions Subtest** This subtest assesses the learner's capitalization and punctuation skills. Students must identify mistakes using a multiple-choice format.

MONITORING PROGRESS

CHAPTER QUIZZES

Each chapter has a two-page quiz with 20 multiple-choice questions and one writing prompt. The following subtests within the Chapter Quizzes reflect the skills that have been taught in the various sections of each chapter. A scoring guide has been included to ensure consistency and fairness.

A. Vocabulary (based on the Build Vocabulary and Word Study sections of the chapter)

B. **Text Structure/Elements of Literature**

C. **Reading Strategies**

D. **Grammar/Usage**

E. **Writing**

UNIT TESTS

Each unit has a six-page test with 40 multiple-choice questions and one writing prompt. There are nine subtests within the Unit Tests. Each subtest reflects the skills within the unit and the skills found on state tests. A scoring guide has been included to ensure consistency and fairness. The nine subtests are as follows:

A. **Reading** Allows students to apply and assess the skills they have learned in the unit.

B. **Reading Comprehension** Assesses literal, inferential, and higher-order thinking through multiple-choice questions.

C. **Reading Strategies** Assesses skills emphasized in Standards Assessment, such as identifying main idea/details, making inferences, drawing conclusions, and so on.

D. **Elements of Literature** Assesses knowledge of literary elements emphasized in Standards Assessment, such as plot, setting, character, point of view, and so on.

E. **Vocabulary** Assesses vocabulary skills emphasized in Standards Assessment, such as prefixes, suffixes, root words, and so on.

F. **Grammar/Usage** Assesses knowledge and skills emphasized in grammar and usage Standards Assessment.

G. **Editing** Assesses students' ability to identify problems in writing and to correct or improve them.

H. Writing Conventions Assesses knowledge and application of spelling, capitalization, and punctuation.

 I. Writing Assesses students' writing skills. The writing prompt is centered on the unit theme. Planning guidelines or tips are included to help students write.

SUMMATIVE EVALUATION

MID-BOOK AND END-OF-BOOK EXAMS

Mid-Book Exam Assesses skills covered in *Visions*, Units 1–3.

End-of-Book Exam Assesses skills covered in *Visions*, Units 1–6.

Both exams reflect the type and nature of testing done on standardized tests. They help prepare students to take language arts and English language-learner types of tests. The nine subtests within each Mid-Book and End-of-Book Exam are the same as the Unit subtests but require more higher-order thinking. Students are required to write a three-paragraph essay in *Visions* A and a five-paragraph essay in *Visions* B & C.

STUDENT RESOURCES

PORTFOLIO ASSESSMENT

Introducing the portfolio

Distribute a folder to each student in the class. Direct students to write their names on their portfolios and make a design, such as a coat-of-arms, that pictorially tells something about them. Write the word *portfolio* on the board and explain that their portfolio is a collection of their best work. At least one piece of their work from each unit should go into their portfolio. Their portfolios should contain the best examples of the effort, progress, and achievements they have made throughout *Visions*.

Student participation in selecting pieces

Students should save all of the work they do in each unit in a "work" folder. At the end of each unit, students will select their best work from this collection to add to their portfolio.

Model the portfolio selection process by distributing the *Portfolio: Activity Rating and Reflection Sheet* (p. 115). Then, write on the board: "What is the piece or activity I liked the most?" Demonstrate removing the selected piece from their work folder and placing it in the portfolio.

Discuss the criteria for selecting pieces

Discuss with the class the reasons for making a portfolio selection. Add their responses to a list on the board. Be sure to explain to students the following characteristics of a portfolio:

> - **It is continuous and ongoing.** A portfolio contains samples of work that stretch over an entire marking period and can be accompanied by art, videotapes, and computer graphics.
> - **It provides for student reflection** about students' own work and learning.
> - **It contains a variety of different assessment tools** including student checklists.

Paulson, F.L., Paulson, P.R., and Meyer, CA. (1991, February). "What Makes a Portfolio a Portfolio?" *Educational Leadership*, pp. 60–63.

Portfolio: Activity Rating and Reflection Sheet

Show students how to fill out the *Portfolio: Activity Rating and Reflection Sheet*. Have students work with a partner to share their work and discuss their responses before completing the sheet. When students have completed the sheet, have them attach it to the piece that they select to place in their portfolio.

Completing the portfolio process

Explain where students should put their portfolios for storage until the next time they use them. Also explain where students should keep their "work" folders. The pieces of work gathered from the unit that were not selected to include in the portfolio may be taken home.

READING FLUENCY

Practice

Throughout *Visions*, students receive practice in all the basic subskills of reading fluency.

VISIONS B   Assessment Program • Copyright © Heinle

Each lesson is designed to cover and scaffold fluency instruction for English language learners. The subskills include word recognition, chunking, phrases, oral reading, silent reading, reading comprehension, adjusting rate for purpose, repeated reading, and reading with expression.

The Reading Fluency Chart (p. 116) serves two assessment purposes. It serves as a record for:

1. The number of words per minute a student reads aloud.
2. The number of words per minute a student reads silently.

After students have recorded their progress on their Reading Fluency Charts, the students' grade level in reading fluency can be determined by referring to the rubric below.

Average rates for reading for students in Grades 2–12

Grade Equivalent	Standard Words per Minute
2.5	121
3.5	135
4.5	149
5.5	163
6.5	177
7.5	191
8.5	205
9.5	219
10.5	233
11.5	247
12.5	261

Source: Carver (1990)
National Center for Education Statistics

CHECKLISTS

Student Checklists are an integral part of the portfolio evaluation process. They provide feedback and a record of student progress in listening, speaking, reading, writing, and viewing. These checklists are referenced in the *Visions* Teacher Editions and are reproducible from the Assessment Program. The checklists and evaluation forms provided are:

Student Checklist	Page
Portfolio: Activity Rating and Reflection Sheet	115
Reading Fluency Chart	116
Responding to Peers' Writing: *EQS*	117
Peer Editing Checklist	118
Editor's Checklist	119–120
Narrative Checklist	121
Persuasive Checklist	122
Oral Presentation Evaluation Sheet	123
Active Listening Checklist	124
Speaking Checklist	125
Viewing Checklist	126
Word Study and Spelling	127
Word Study and Spelling Assessment Chart	128
Independent Reading Record	129
Student Self-Assessment	130
Activity and Project Reflection	131
Test-Taking Tips	132–133

TEACHER RESOURCES

CHECKLISTS

The Teacher Resource reproducible checklists should be used to plan and evaluate instruction. The *Lesson Plan Checklist for The Sheltered Instruction Observation Protocol* (*SIOP*) (pp. 134–135) can be used during the Across Content Areas sections of *Visions*. The *Rubric for Oral Reading Fluency* (p. 136) will help you assess the progress of your students during the Build Reading Fluency sections of the student book. You may want to give students a copy of the *Rubric for Oral Presentations* (p. 137) that you will use for grading. The following important checklists serve as a guideline for standards-based accountability. Four marking periods are provided for each standard.

- Listening and Speaking Standards Assessment Checklist, pp. 138–139
- Reading Standards Assessment Checklist, pp. 140–141
- Writing Standards Assessment Checklist, pp. 142–143
- Viewing and Representing Standards Assessment Checklist, p. 144

Name _____ Date _____

Answer Sheet

For Diagnostic Test, Unit Tests, Mid-Book Exam, and End-of-Book Exam

Fill in the circles of the correct answers. Erase mistakes well.

☐ **Diagnostic Test**

☐ **Unit _____ Test**

☐ **Mid-Book Exam**

☐ **End-of-Book Exam**

1. ⓐⓑⓒⓓ	11. ⓐⓑⓒⓓ	21. ⓐⓑⓒⓓ	31. ⓐⓑⓒⓓ
2. ⓐⓑⓒⓓ	12. ⓐⓑⓒⓓ	22. ⓐⓑⓒⓓ	32. ⓐⓑⓒⓓ
3. ⓐⓑⓒⓓ	13. ⓐⓑⓒⓓ	23. ⓐⓑⓒⓓ	33. ⓐⓑⓒⓓ
4. ⓐⓑⓒⓓ	14. ⓐⓑⓒⓓ	24. ⓐⓑⓒⓓ	34. ⓐⓑⓒⓓ
5. ⓐⓑⓒⓓ	15. ⓐⓑⓒⓓ	25. ⓐⓑⓒⓓ	35. ⓐⓑⓒⓓ
6. ⓐⓑⓒⓓ	16. ⓐⓑⓒⓓ	26. ⓐⓑⓒⓓ	36. ⓐⓑⓒⓓ
7. ⓐⓑⓒⓓ	17. ⓐⓑⓒⓓ	27. ⓐⓑⓒⓓ	37. ⓐⓑⓒⓓ
8. ⓐⓑⓒⓓ	18. ⓐⓑⓒⓓ	28. ⓐⓑⓒⓓ	38. ⓐⓑⓒⓓ
9. ⓐⓑⓒⓓ	19. ⓐⓑⓒⓓ	29. ⓐⓑⓒⓓ	39. ⓐⓑⓒⓓ
10. ⓐⓑⓒⓓ	20. ⓐⓑⓒⓓ	30. ⓐⓑⓒⓓ	40. ⓐⓑⓒⓓ

VISIONS B Assessment Program • Copyright © Heinle

Answer Sheet
For Chapter Quizzes

Fill in the circles of the correct answers. Erase mistakes well.

Chapter _____ Quiz

1. ⓐ ⓑ ⓒ ⓓ   11. ⓐ ⓑ ⓒ ⓓ

2. ⓐ ⓑ ⓒ ⓓ   12. ⓐ ⓑ ⓒ ⓓ

3. ⓐ ⓑ ⓒ ⓓ   13. ⓐ ⓑ ⓒ ⓓ

4. ⓐ ⓑ ⓒ ⓓ   14. ⓐ ⓑ ⓒ ⓓ

5. ⓐ ⓑ ⓒ ⓓ   15. ⓐ ⓑ ⓒ ⓓ

6. ⓐ ⓑ ⓒ ⓓ   16. ⓐ ⓑ ⓒ ⓓ

7. ⓐ ⓑ ⓒ ⓓ   17. ⓐ ⓑ ⓒ ⓓ

8. ⓐ ⓑ ⓒ ⓓ   18. ⓐ ⓑ ⓒ ⓓ

9. ⓐ ⓑ ⓒ ⓓ   19. ⓐ ⓑ ⓒ ⓓ

10. ⓐ ⓑ ⓒ ⓓ   20. ⓐ ⓑ ⓒ ⓓ

Diagnostic Test Results Chart

Record students' scores for each section of the diagnostic test here.

Student Name	A. Vocabulary Meaning	B. Word Study	C. Reading Comprehension	D. Reading Strategies	E. Grammar/ Usage	F. Spelling	G. Writing	H. Writing Conventions
1.								
2.								
3.								
4.								
5.								
6.								
7.								
8.								
9.								
10.								
11.								
12.								
13.								
14.								
15.								
16.								
17.								

VISIONS B Assessment Program • Copyright © Heinle

Intervention/Reteaching Component Guide

This chart serves as a guide to the *Visions* components you can use to reteach the skills tested on the Unit Tests, the Mid-Book Exam, and the End-of-Book Exam.

	Student Book	Teacher Edition	Activity Book	Student Handbook	Student CD-ROM	More Grammar Practice workbook	Teacher Resource Book
A. Reading Comprehension	X	X			X		
B. Reading Strategies	X	X		X	X		X
C. Elements of Literature	X	X	X	X	X		
D. Vocabulary	X		X	X	X		X
E. Grammar/ Usage	X		X	X	X	X	
F. Editing				X			
G. Writing Conventions		X	X	X	X		
H. Writing	X		X	X			X

Student Name _____

Individual Progress Chart for Intervention
Chapter Quizzes

The purpose of this chart is to record the student's progress and to use it as a basis for intervention and reteaching. Note sub-sections of the quizzes where the student is weak and target those areas as part of the intervention plan.

Formal Assessment

Record the student's scores for each sub-section of the quizzes.

Write the number correct over the number of possible points for each sub-section.

	Unit 1					Unit 2					Unit 3					Unit 4				Unit 5				Unit 6			
	1	2	3	4	5	1	2	3	4	5	1	2	3	4	5	1	2	3	4	1	2	3	4	1	2	3	4
A. Vocabulary	/	/	/	/	/	/	/	/	/	/	/	/	/	/	/	/	/	/	/	/	/	/	/	/	/	/	/
B. Text Structure/ Elements of Literature	/	/	/	/	/	/	/	/	/	/	/	/	/	/	/	/	/	/	/	/	/	/	/	/	/	/	/
C. Reading Strategies	/	/	/	/	/	/	/	/	/	/	/	/	/	/	/	/	/	/	/	/	/	/	/	/	/	/	/
D. Grammar/ Usage	/	/	/	/	/	/	/	/	/	/	/	/	/	/	/	/	/	/	/	/	/	/	/	/	/	/	/
E. Writing	/	/	/	/	/	/	/	/	/	/	/	/	/	/	/	/	/	/	/	/	/	/	/	/	/	/	/

Student Name _____

Individual Progress Chart for Intervention
Unit Tests, Mid-Book Exam, End-of-Book Exam

The purpose of this chart is to record the student's progress and to use it as a basis for intervention and reteaching. Note sub-sections of the tests where the student is weak and target those areas as part of the intervention plan.

Formal Assessment

Write the number correct over the number of possible points for each sub-section.

	Unit 1 Test	Unit 2 Test	Unit 3 Test	Mid-Book Exam	Unit 4 Test	Unit 5 Test	Unit 6 Test	End-of-Book Exam
Reading Comprehension	/20	/20	/20	/20	/20	/20	/20	/20
Reading Strategies	/10	/10	/10	/10	/10	/10	/10	/10
Elements of Literature	/10	/10	/10	/10	/10	/10	/10	/10
Vocabulary	/10	/10	/10	/10	/10	/10	/10	/10
Grammar/Usage	/10	/10	/10	/10	/10	/10	/10	/10
Editing	/10	/10	/10	/10	/10	/10	/10	/10
Writing Conventions	/10	/10	/10	/10	/10	/10	/10	/10
Writing	/20	/20	/20	/20	/20	/20	/20	/20

Authentic Assessment

Record your observations of the student's strengths and needs.

Student Portfolio	Teacher Observation (language development, content, organization, creativity, other)
Unit 1	
Unit 2	
Unit 3	
Unit 4	
Unit 5	
Unit 6	

Interpersonal Skills	Teacher Observation (participation, cooperation, other)
Unit 1	
Unit 2	
Unit 3	
Unit 4	
Unit 5	
Unit 6	

Holistic Scoring Guide for Writing Assessment

	20 points	15 points	10 points	5 points
Development of Ideas Are ideas presented and supported insightfully?	• Ideas are thoroughly developed. • Development reflects thought. • Ideas are presented insightfully. • Compositional risks enhance writing.	• Ideas are reasonably well-developed. • Development shows thought. • Ideas show thought. • Few compositional risks evident.	• Idea development is attempted. • Omitted information creates minor gaps between ideas.	• Little or no idea development is evident. • Ideas are a summary of a known writing, movie, or TV show. • Omitted information creates significant gaps between ideas.
Organization Are ideas ordered logically from sentence to paragraph?	• Thought progression is smooth and controlled. • Transitions are meaningful. • Order of ideas is logical. • Organizational strategies enhance presentation of ideas.	• Thought progression is generally smooth and controlled. • Transitions are mostly meaningful. • Ideas are mostly linked. • Effective organizational strategies. • Minor wordiness and/or repetition.	• Thought progression is somewhat smooth and logical. • More transitions are needed. • Ideas are somewhat linked. • Ineffective organizational strategy. • Some wordiness and/or repetition.	• Progression of thought is not logical. • Inappropriate use or lack of transitions. • There is no organizational strategy. • Wordiness and/or repetition inhibits progression of ideas.
Voice Does the writer engage the reader and express his/her individuality?	• Reader is engaged throughout. • Composition sounds original. • Individuality and unique voice are expressed.	• Reader is generally engaged. • In general, composition sounds original. • Writing generally expresses individuality.	• Reader is engaged sporadically. • Parts of the composition sound original. • Writing expresses some individuality.	• Writing does not engage the reader. • Little or no sense of the writer's voice. • Composition does not sound original. • Writing does not express individuality.
Fluency and Focus How well do individual paragraphs and the whole composition flow together?	• Focus is sustained throughout. • Writing has sense of completeness. • Introduction/conclusion are meaningful. • All/most of writing contributes to development and quality.	• Writing is generally focused. • Clear relationship between ideas. • Few sudden shifts in ideas. • Overall sense of completeness. • Introduction/conclusion add depth. • Most of writing contributes to development and quality.	• Writing is somewhat focused. • Writer shifts ideas, but ideas are related. • Some sense of completeness. • Introduction/conclusion are superficial. • Some of writing is extraneous.	• Writing is not focused. • Writer shifts ideas abruptly. • Little or no sense of completeness. • Introduction/conclusion are inadequate. • Much of writing is extraneous. • Connection to prompt is weak.
Conventions Are spelling, capitalization, punctuation, grammar, usage, and sentence structure appropriate?	• Writing shows a strong/consistent command of conventions. • Minor errors occur during compositional risks. • Words, phrases, and sentence structure enhance effectiveness.	• Writing shows good command of conventions. • Minor errors do not disrupt fluency. • Words, phrases, and sentence structure are generally appropriate and contribute to effectiveness.	• Writing shows limited control of conventions. • Errors weaken fluency. • Simple or inaccurate words and phrases and awkward sentences limit effectiveness.	• Writing has severe/frequent errors in conventions. • There is an overall lack of fluency. • There is frequent misuse/omission of words and phrases. • Frequent use of awkward sentences.
Presentation Does format ease and enhance understanding?	• Penmanship is pleasing. • Margins and spacing enhance understanding. • Devices (headings, bullets, numbers, etc.) clarify and organize information.	• Penmanship is clear. • Margins and spacing are appropriate. • Devices (headings, bullets, numbers, etc.) are somewhat effective.	• Penmanship is difficult to interpret. • Margins and spacing are inconsistent. • Devices (headings, bullets, numbers, etc.) are superficial.	• Penmanship is illegible. • Margins and spacing are confusing. • Inappropriate use or lack of devices (headings, bullets, numbers, etc.).

VISIONS B Assessment Program • Copyright © Heinle

Name _____ Date _____

DIAGNOSTIC TEST

A. ➤ **Vocabulary Meaning:** Choose the correct answer. *(10 points)*

1. A *challenge* is something that is _____ to do.
   a. difficult
   b. easy
   c. sad
   d. silly

2. To *discover* something is to _____ it.
   a. cover
   b. change
   c. find
   d. bury

3. The horse *galloped* down the street, crashing into people as it went. *Galloped* means _____.
   a. ate
   b. walked
   c. went fast
   d. yelled

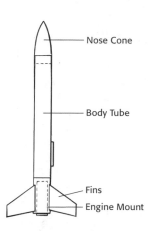

Nose Cone

Body Tube

Fins

Engine Mount

4. Look at the diagram of a rocket. The top of the rocket is called the _____.
   a. engine mount
   b. nose cone
   c. body tube
   d. fins

5. _____ are on either side of the rocket.
   a. Engine mounts
   b. Fins
   c. Nose cones
   d. Body tubes

B. ➤ **Word Study:** Choose the correct answer. *(10 points)*

6. The two words that make the compound word *fingernails* are _____.
   a. *fin* and *gernails*
   b. *fing* and *ernails*
   c. *finger* and *nails*
   d. *fingernail* and *s*

7. Lara paints beautiful pictures of the ocean. Lara is a _____.
   a. picturer
   b. painter
   c. dancer
   d. picture

8. Which word begins with the same sound as *physical*?
   a. syllable
   b. phonics
   c. picture
   d. wiggle

---

sea·son /'sizən/ *n.* **1** a three-month period: *Summer and fall are her favorite seasons.* **2** a time for a certain activity: *In some states the hunting season begins September 1.* *-v.* **3** to add spices or flavoring to food: *We season our vegetables with a little salt and garlic.* **4** to age s.t. properly: *to season wood for lumber*

---

9. Look at the dictionary entry. Which definition is used in this sentence? *Be sure to <u>season</u> the soup.*
   a. 1
   b. 2
   c. 3
   d. 4

10. What part of speech can the word *season* be?
    a. verb
    b. adjective
    c. adverb
    d. preposition

DIAGNOSTIC TEST (continued)

C. ➤ Reading Comprehension: Choose the correct answer based on the readings. (20 points)

Reading 1: Road Signs

1 There are two kinds of road signs. Some have words on them. Others do not. Here are some common road signs.

2 Road signs have special shapes. For example, all warning signs look like diamonds. All stop signs have eight sides. Railroad signs are circles. Upside-down triangles mean "yield." A yield sign is almost like a stop sign. A *yield* sign means "let other cars go first."

3 Stop signs are always red. The word STOP is usually on them. Yield signs are yellow. They sometimes have the word YIELD on them. Many warning signs are yellow. Most other signs are black and white. They tell about situations on the road. Here are some more examples:

11. How many kinds of road signs are there?
    a. two
    b. five
    c. eight
    d. more than ten

12. How many sides does a stop sign have?
    a. two   c. six
    b. eight   d. four

13. What color are many warning signs?
    a. yellow   c. black
    b. red   d. green

14. A "yield" sign _____.
    a. is red
    b. is a square
    c. has six sides
    d. means you let others go first

15. What is true about all road signs?
    a. They are the same color.
    b. They are the same shape.
    c. They have words on them.
    d. They tell drivers what to do on the road.

VISIONS B Assessment Program • Copyright © Heinle

DIAGNOSTIC TEST (continued)

Reading 2: The New York City Marathon: A World Race

1   Fred LeBow started the New York City Marathon. It began in 1970 as a small race. Only 127 people ran, and only 55 of them finished. They ran around Central Park four times. Not many people watched them run. However, the marathon grew over the years and became more popular.

2   Today, thirty thousand people come from all over the world to run in the marathon. They run through different parts of New York City. Over two million people come to cheer runners in the marathon that became a world race.

New York City Marathon, 2002 Female Winners			
Place	Name	Time	Country
1	Joyce Chepchumba	2:25:56	Kenya
2	Lyubov Denisova	2:26:17	Russia
3	Esther Kiplagat	2:27:00	Kenya
4	Marla Runyan	2:27:10	USA
5	Margaret Okayo	2:27:46	Kenya
6	Kerryn McCann	2:27:51	Australia
7	Lornah Kiplagat	2:28:41	Kenya
8	Ludmila Petrova	2:29:00	Russia
9	Milena Glusac	2:31:14	USA
10	Zinaida Semyonova	2:31:39	Russia

16. Who started the New York City Marathon?
    a. Marla Runyan
    b. Joyce Chepchumba
    c. Milena Glusac
    d. Fred LeBow

17. In the first New York City Marathon, _____.
    a. there were 127 runners
    b. there were 55 runners
    c. Fred LeBow was the only runner
    d. there were 30,000 runners

18. Look at the chart. Which country had the most runners?
    a. Australia   c. Russia
    b. Kenya   d. USA

19. Look at the chart. What country is Lyubov Denisova from?
    a. Kenya
    b. Russia
    c. USA
    d. Australia

20. Look at the chart. How much time did it take Kerryn McCann to run the marathon?
    a. 2:25:56
    b. 2:31:14
    c. 2:27:51
    d. 2:28:41

DIAGNOSTIC TEST (continued)

D. ➤ **Reading Strategies**: Choose the correct answer based on the readings. *(20 points)*

21. You can infer from the reading that this road sign is probably _____.
  a. red
  b. green
  c. yellow
  d. black and white

22. What is the main idea of paragraph 2 of *Road Signs?*
  a. There are two kinds of road signs.
  b. Road signs have special shapes.
  c. Many warning signs are yellow.
  d. Stop signs are always red.

23. What is the main idea of paragraph 2 of *The New York City Marathon?*
  a. The marathon is not popular.
  b. The marathon is in New York City.
  c. The New York City Marathon is now a world race.
  d. Thirty thousand people run in the marathon today.

24. From *The New York City Marathon*, you can infer that _____.
  a. The people of New York do not like the marathon.
  b. You have to live in New York to run in the marathon.
  c. You must live in Kenya to run in the marathon.
  d. The New York City Marathon is popular.

25. Which of these statements is an opinion?
  a. Over two million people come to watch the race today.
  b. I think running is the best exercise.
  c. Fred LeBow started the New York City Marathon.
  d. Joyce Chepchumba was the fastest female runner.

Name _____ Date _____

DIAGNOSTIC TEST *(continued)*

E. ➤ **Grammar/Usage:** Choose the correct answer. *(10 points)*

26. Miguel _____ sick yesterday.
 a. be
 b. is
 c. was
 d. were

27. They _____ dinner at 6 o'clock every night.
 a. eat
 b. eats
 c. is eat
 d. be eat

28. I have not seen my best friend since _____ moved away.
 a. he
 b. him
 c. it
 d. they

29. Marta _____ swim well when she was young.
 a. can
 b. could
 c. should
 d. does

30. Lara _____ to art lessons after school every day for the past five years.
 a. goed
 b. is going
 c. been going
 d. has been going

F. ➤ **Spelling:** Choose the correct answer. *(10 points)*

31. We have beautiful _____ in the garden.
 a. flours
 b. flowers
 c. flower
 d. flouers

32. He _____ the door on his way out.
 a. slamt
 b. slamd
 c. slammed
 d. eslammed

33. The word *seal* rhymes (has the same vowel sound) with _____.
 a. feel
 b. fail
 c. sell
 d. well

34. _____ hot outside. Let's go swimming!
 a. It
 b. Is
 c. Its
 d. It's

35. Which word has an "*f*" sound in it?
 a. photo
 b. night
 c. room
 d. sixty

DIAGNOSTIC TEST *(continued)*

G. ➤ Writing: Write a paragraph about the topic below. Write your paragraph on a piece of paper. *(20 points)*

> **Writing Prompt** Describe something you have done that was fun for you.

H. ➤ Writing Conventions: There is one mistake in each sentence. Choose the letter which is under the mistake.
(10 points)

36. the Boston Marathon is a popular race in
    a   b   c
    Massachusetts.
          d

37. The race is Twenty-six miles long.
    a   b   c   d

38. Can you run for twenty-six miles.
    a   b   c   d

39. Before they run the race, "runners" must
         a   b   c
    be ready.
       d

40. "They all ran great," "said Bob".
          a   b   c   d

QUIZ Unit 1 • Chapter 1

A. ➤ Vocabulary: Choose the correct answer. *(24 points: 4 points each)*

1. Two words that have similar meanings are _____.
   a. inferences
   b. suffixes
   c. synonyms
   d. rhyming words

2. We awoke at <u>dawn</u>. A synonym for <u>dawn</u> is _____.
   a. suntan
   b. sunrise
   c. sunset
   d. sunshine

3. In this dictionary entry, what word is listed as the synonym of <u>fatigue</u>?
   a. great tiredness
   b. military
   c. exhaustion
   d. soldiers

> **fatigue** /fəˈtig/ *n.* **1** great tiredness, (*syn.*) exhaustion: *He is suffering from fatigue and wants to go to bed early.* **2** *pl.* military clothes: *Soldiers wear fatigues.*

4. A _____ is a group of letters added to the end of a word.
   a. noun
   b. verb
   c. prefix
   d. suffix

5. A person who speaks is called a _____.
   a. speaking
   b. speaked
   c. speaker
   d. speakier

6. A person who races is called a _____.
   a. racier
   b. racer
   c. eraser
   d. erased

B. ➤ Test Structure/Elements of Literature: Read and choose the correct answer. *(28 points: 4 points each)*

> "Star Light, Star Bright"
>
> 1 Star light, star bright
>   first star I see tonight
>
> 2 I wish I may, I wish I might
>   Have the wish I wish tonight

7. Which words rhyme?
   a. light/star
   b. may/wish
   c. bright/might
   d. star/tonight

8. A stanza is _____.
   a. the ending of a poem
   b. the beginning of a poem
   c. a group of lines in a poem
   d. the title of a poem

9. How many stanzas are in this poem?
   a. 0
   b. 1
   c. 2
   d. 4

> "The Tortoise and the Hare"
>
> 1 One day a hare laughed at a tortoise for moving so slowly. The tortoise challenged the hare to a race. The hare laughed, but agreed.
> 2 When the race began, the hare ran quickly ahead. When he saw the tortoise far behind him, the hare lay down on the side of the road and fell asleep. The tortoise never stopped for a moment and reached the finish line before the hare woke up.
>
> –Aesop

QUIZ Unit 1 • Chapter 1 (continued)

10. "The Tortoise and the Hare" is an example of a _____.
    a. play
    b. poem
    c. fable
    d. historical narrative

11. Choose the moral that best fits "The Tortoise and the Hare."
    a. Tortoises are slow animals.
    b. Slow and steady wins the race.
    c. It is important to get enough sleep.
    d. Hares are not nice animals.

12. The main character of a fable is usually a(n) _____.
    a. hare
    b. person
    c. object
    d. animal

13. Rhyming words in a poem have _____.
    a. the same ending sound
    b. the same beginning sound
    c. different ending sounds
    d. capital letters

C. ➤ Reading Strategies: Choose the correct answer. *(12 points: 4 points each)*

14. To make an inference is to _____.
    a. arrange information in a sequence
    b. use what you know to make a guess
    c. study the role of each character
    d. record the events of a story

15. Rosa entered a running race and won. You can infer that _____.
    a. Rosa was the fastest runner
    b. Rosa was very sad
    c. there were many racers in the race
    d. the race was on Saturday

16. There was no applause at the end of Camel's dance. You can infer that _____.
    a. Camel's dance was great
    b. the audience didn't like the dance
    c. Camel bowed at the end of her dance
    d. the audience thought that the dance was happy

D. ➤ Grammar/Usage: Choose the correct answer. *(16 points: 4 points each)*

17. Yesterday, Martha _____ to her friend on the phone.
    a. talks
    b. will talk
    c. talking
    d. talked

18. Juan _____ sick this morning, so he stayed home from school.
    a. feels
    b. feeling
    c. felt
    d. feeled

19. Which verb is irregular?
    a. watch/watched
    b. call/called
    c. rain/rained
    d. eat/ate

20. Which verb is regular?
    a. sing/sang
    b. live/lived
    c. think/thought
    d. catch/caught

E. ➤ Writing *(20 points)*

> **Writing Prompt** Write a paragraph to describe a challenge that you, or someone you know, faced. Explain what you did to face the challenge.

QUIZ Unit 1 • Chapter 2

A. ➤ Vocabulary: Choose the correct answer. *(24 points: 4 points each)*

1. A reader can guess the meanings of new words by using the _____.
   a. dictionary
   b. context
   c. definition
   d. meaning

2. The cat was <u>abandoned</u>, so the man took care of it. <u>Abandoned</u> means _____.
   a. left
   b. stopped
   c. fed
   d. worried

3. The <u>climate</u> in the mountains is very cold and snowy. <u>Climate</u> means _____.
   a. tree
   b. river
   c. weather
   d. height

4. Words that are made up of two other words are called _____.
   a. compound words
   b. adjectives
   c. prefixes
   d. suffixes

5. The smell of the popcorn is making me hungry. The compound word in the sentence is _____.
   a. smell
   b. popcorn
   c. making
   d. hungry

6. She chose the blue sunglasses. The compound word in the sentence is _____.
   a. she
   b. chose
   c. blue
   d. sunglasses

B. ➤ Text Structure/Elements of Literature: Read and choose the correct answer. *(32 points: 4 points each)*

"Rosa's Race"

1   Rosa's team was standing on the other side of the pool. Rosa knew she must swim across the pool. She had learned how to swim at the community center. Rosa jumped into the pool. She could not believe it. She was swimming like a fish. Rosa could hear her teammates yelling and clapping for her. Pete was swimming close by. Rosa knew she could beat Pete and help her team win.

7. "Rosa's Race" is an example of a _____.
   a. realistic adventure fiction
   b. personal narrative
   c. poem
   d. fable

8. Where does the story take place?
   a. at Rosa's house
   b. at Pete's house
   c. at a community center
   d. at a pool

9. What is the problem in the story?
   a. Rosa's team left her.
   b. Rosa has to beat Pete across the pool.
   c. Pete will not clap for Rosa.
   d. Pete cannot swim.

10. Which word best describes Rosa?
    a. brave
    b. sad
    c. upset
    d. scared

QUIZ Unit 1 • Chapter 2 (continued)

11. A simile shows a comparison by using the words _____.
    a. *like* or *as*
    b. *if* or *the*
    c. *could* or *not*
    d. *in* or *of*

12. Which sentence contains a simile?
    a. The cat slept peacefully.
    b. The wind blew fiercely.
    c. She likes to read lots of books.
    d. His smile is as wide as the sea.

13. Which sentence from the story contains a simile?
    a. Rosa jumped into the pool.
    b. She could not believe it.
    c. She was swimming like a fish.
    d. Pete was swimming close by.

14. Similes are a type of _____.
    a. flashback
    b. setting
    c. figurative language
    d. foreshadowing

C. ➤ Reading Strategies: Choose the correct answer. *(12 points: 4 points each)*

15. An action or event that makes something happen is called the _____.
    a. effect
    b. problem
    c. cause
    d. solution

16. The result of the action or event is called the _____.
    a. meaning
    b. effect
    c. connection
    d. cause

17. Wade forgot to get gas for his car. Which of these is a likely effect?
    a. Wade makes gas for his car.
    b. Wade gets another car.
    c. Wade drives more slowly.
    d. Wade's car runs out of gas.

D. ➤ Grammar/Usage: Choose the correct answer. *(12 points: 4 points each)*

18. The verb <u>be</u> is a(n) _____.
    a. regular verb
    b. irregular verb
    c. past tense verb
    d. possessive verb

19. Last week, they _____ on vacation.
    a. is
    b. are
    c. was
    d. were

20. Yesterday, Brian _____ in the forest.
    a. was
    b. is
    c. will be
    d. were

E. ➤ Writing *(20 points)*

> **Writing Prompt** Write a paragraph about a realistic adventure. Make up a character with a challenge to face. Describe how the character meets the challenge.

QUIZ Unit 1 • Chapter3

A. ➤ Vocabulary: Choose the correct answer. *(24 points: 4 points each)*

1. The _____ is the back of a ship.
   a. sail
   b. stern
   c. rudder
   d. deck

2. Wind blowing into the _____ makes a ship move.
   a. decks
   b. bow
   c. sails
   d. stern

3. Words that describe verbs are called _____.
   a. adjectives
   b. nouns
   c. adverbs
   d. similes

4. The sailors quickly abandoned the sinking ship. The adverb in the sentence is _____.
   a. sailors
   b. quickly
   c. abandoned
   d. sinking

5. Esther quietly hummed a song. The adverb in the sentence is _____.
   a. quietly
   b. hummed
   c. Esther
   d. song

6. The bird flew swiftly to its nest. The adverb in the sentence is _____.
   a. bird
   b. flew
   c. swiftly
   d. nest

B. ➤ Text Structure/Elements of Literature: Read and choose the correct answer. *(28 points: 4 points each)*

> "Beginning the Voyage"
>
> 1 On Friday, August 3, 1492, three ships set sail from Spain. Christopher Columbus and some of his helpers were on board one of the ships. More helpers were on board the other two ships. They waved goodbye to their families from the decks of the ships. The helpers' families watched as the ships swam lazily into the sea.

7. This reading is an example of _____.
   a. a historical narrative
   b. a personal narrative
   c. poetry
   d. fantasy

8. _____ gives human thoughts, feelings, and actions to an object or animal.
   a. Personification
   b. Nonfiction
   c. A narrative
   d. An exclamation

9. Which phrase from "Beginning the Voyage" is an example of personification?
   a. sailed away from Spain
   b. some of his helpers
   c. the other two ships
   d. the ships swam lazily

10. Which of these phrases from "Beginning the Voyage" places the story in history?
    a. On Friday, August 3, 1492
    b. set sail from Spain
    c. They waved goodbye
    d. ships swam lazily

QUIZ Unit 1 • Chapter 3 (continued)

11. Christopher Columbus is _____.
    a. one of the ships from the story
    b. another name for the story
    c. the name of the country in the story
    d. the name of a real person from the story

12. What is the setting of the story?
    a. Spain
    b. America
    c. a helper's house
    d. Christopher Columbus's house

13. The ships swam lazily means the ships _____.
    a. did not sink
    b. were tired
    c. stopped suddenly
    d. moved slowly

C. ➤ **Reading Strategies:** Choose the correct answer. *(12 points: 4 points each)*

14. Predicting is when the reader _____.
    a. reads the whole story without stopping
    b. describes the setting of the story
    c. writes the story in his or her own words
    d. guesses what will happen next

15. Mario and Ramon are playing baseball. It starts to rain very hard. Which sentence best predicts what will happen next?
    a. Mario and Ramon will continue to play in the rain.
    b. Mario and Ramon will look for shelter from the rain.
    c. Mario and Ramon will invite friends to play.
    d. Mario and Ramon will use another bat and ball.

16. The candles on Jamaica's birthday cake are lit. She makes a wish and then blows out the candles. Which sentence best predicts what will happen next?
    a. Jamaica will eat the cake.
    b. Jamaica will make a cake.
    c. Jamaica will go to a party.
    d. Jamaica will fall asleep.

D. ➤ **Grammar/Usage:** Choose the correct answer. *(16 points: 4 points each)*

17. The word and can mean _____.
    a. also
    b. never
    c. maybe
    d. or

18. Apples are fruits. Oranges are fruits. What is the best way to combine these two sentences?
    a. Oranges fruits and apples.
    b. Apples and oranges are fruits.
    c. Fruits are oranges but apples.
    d. Apples or oranges fruit.

19. I am tired. I am sleepy. What is the best way to combine these two sentences?
    a. Because I am sleepy tired.
    b. So I am tired then sleepy.
    c. I am sleepy but tired.
    d. I am tired and sleepy.

20. The juice was cold. The juice was sweet. What is the best way to combine these two sentences?
    a. And there was cold sweet juice.
    b. The juice was cold and sweet.
    c. The cold juice or the sweet juice.
    d. Two cold, sweet juices.

E. ➤ **Writing** *(20 points)*

> **Writing Prompt** Write a nonfiction historical narrative. Write about someone that you have learned about who lived long ago. Use time words in your writing.

VISIONS QUIZ Unit 1 • Chapter 3

VISIONS B Assessment Program • Copyright © Heinle

QUIZ Unit 1 • Chapter 4

A. ➤ Vocabulary: Choose the correct answer. *(24 points: 4 points each)*

1. _____ are words that are pronounced and spelled the same but have different meanings.
   a. Verbs
   b. Synonyms
   c. Adjectives
   d. Homonyms

2. My neighbor is a <u>kind</u> woman. In this sentence <u>kind</u> means _____.
   a. friendly
   b. same
   c. different
   d. honest

3. Hector lives in a four-<u>story</u> apartment building. In this sentence <u>story</u> means _____.
   a. a type of book
   b. telling about an adventure
   c. a floor in a building
   d. not telling the truth

4. Lydia plays the drums in a <u>band</u>. Which sentence has the same meaning of <u>band</u> as it is used in this sentence?
   a. Put a rubber band around the newspaper.
   b. We danced to music from a live band.
   c. The band keeps Sung's hair off of her face.
   d. The band on my watch is too tight.

5. *Spect* means _____ in Latin.
   a. to hide
   b. to look
   c. to shorten
   d. quickly

6. Respect means _____.
   a. to look at closely
   b. to hide something
   c. to look at with approval
   d. to see if someone has something

B. ➤ Text Structure/Elements of Literature: Read and choose the correct answer. *(24 points: 4 points each)*

> "Travel Plans"
>
> 1   I was excited to visit my cousin in Texas. I was also scared. It was my first trip by airplane. It was also my first trip without my parents. The flight attendant promised to look after me during the plane ride.
>
> 2   I was happy to arrive safely in Texas. I thanked the flight attendant for helping me. I saw my cousin waiting nearby. She smiled and waved.

7. "Travel Plans" is an example of a _____.
   a. poem
   b. fantasy
   c. biography
   d. first-person narrative

8. What is the problem in "Travel Plans"?
   a. The speaker in the story does not want to visit her cousin.
   b. The speaker in the story had never been on a plane before.
   c. The plane ride is too long.
   d. The plane is late in to Texas.

9. "I was excited to visit my cousin in Texas." This sentence is an example of _____.
   a. personification
   b. direct characterization
   c. vocabulary in context
   d. adjectives

10. In a first-person narrative, the speaker tells about _____.
    a. his or her life
    b. how to do something
    c. the adventures of a friend
    d. the history of another person

13

QUIZ Unit 1 • Chapter 4 (continued)

11. "She smiled and waved." What does this sentence from the story tell you about the cousin?
    a. She felt confused.
    b. She was lonely.
    c. She was happy.
    d. She wanted to go home.

12. Which phrase from the story uses a personal pronoun?
    a. in Texas
    b. I was excited
    c. was also scared
    d. the flight attendant

C. ➤ Reading Strategies: Choose the correct answer. (12 points: 4 points each)

13. Comparing your experiences to what happens in a story can help you to _____.
    a. read difficult words in the story
    b. understand the events of the story
    c. compare two characters in the story
    d. predict what the story will be about

14. This is Kevin's first day at a new school. Who would understand how he feels?
    a. someone who likes to be first in everything
    b. someone whose name is also Kevin
    c. someone watching a movie about a new school
    d. someone who has gone to a new school

15. Maribel is excited because she caught a big fish. Who would understand how Maribel feels?
    a. someone who has a fish tank
    b. someone who lives near a beach
    c. someone who goes swimming
    d. someone who likes to go fishing

D. ➤ Grammar/Usage: Choose the correct answer. (20 points: 4 points each)

16. A(n) _____ is part of a sentence that has a subject and a verb.
    a. question
    b. statement
    c. clause
    d. exclamation

17. Time clauses _____.
    a. must be used with main clauses
    b. are independent clauses
    c. only have nouns in them
    d. only have verbs in them

18. While Amiri set the table, Addie poured the milk. Which is the dependent clause?
    a. While Amiri set the table
    b. Addie poured the milk
    c. set the table
    d. poured the milk

19. Grandmother always bakes bread when we visit. Which is the dependent clause?
    a. Grandmother always bakes
    b. when we visit
    c. bakes bread
    d. to visit

20. Lupe finished her homework before dinner was ready. Which is the dependent clause?
    a. before dinner was ready
    b. finished her homework
    c. Lupe finished
    d. was ready

E. ➤ Writing (20 points)

Writing Prompt Write a first-person narrative about something you were afraid of in the past. Use pronouns in your narrative.

VISIONS B Assessment Program • Copyright © Heinle

VISIONS QUIZ Unit 1 • Chapter 5

VISIONS B Assessment Program • Copyright © Heinle

QUIZ Unit 1 • Chapter 5

A. ➤ **Vocabulary:** Choose the correct answer. *(32 points: 4 points each)*

1. Our cat is very agile. He climbs trees quickly and easily. Which word best explains the meaning of agile?
   a. afraid
   b. able to move well
   c. able to read quickly
   d. able to eat quickly

2. I cried out in dismay when I saw the ball hit my neighbor's window and break it. Which word best explains the meaning of dismay?
   a. delight
   b. excitement
   c. unhappiness
   d. anger

3. I was in shock when I learned that I won the grand prize. Which word best explains the meaning of in shock?
   a. very surprised
   b. very angry
   c. nervous
   d. hopeless

4. He muttered something under his breath that I could not understand. Which word best explains the meaning of muttered?
   a. stated clearly
   b. said loudly
   c. sang brightly
   d. said quietly and unclearly

5. The kitten was helpless after it climbed up the tree. The root word of helpless is _____.
   a. he
   b. help
   c. helpless
   d. less

6. I had to rewrite my lost report. The root word of rewrite is _____.
   a. re
   b. write
   c. rewrite
   d. ite

7. Raymond unlocked the door for us. Which word from the sentence contains a root word?
   a. Raymond
   b. unlocked
   c. door
   d. for

8. The baker went to work very early each day. Which word contains a root word?
   a. baker
   b. went
   c. work
   d. day

B. ➤ **Text Structure/Elements of Literature:** Read and choose the correct answer. *(16 points: 4 points each)*

"Saturday Plans"

1   "It's not fair!" said Maya. "I always have to watch the twins. I want to go out with my friends."

2   Maya's father sighed. "I'm sorry, Maya, but I have to rake the leaves. I really need you to watch your brothers." Maya slumped onto the couch.

3   Her father sat beside Maya. "I have an idea. Why don't you ask a friend to come over?"

9. "Saturday Plans" is an example of _____.
   a. poetry
   b. fantasy
   c. a short story
   d. a first-person narrative

10. "It's not fair!" This sentence from the story is an example of _____.
   a. characters
   b. the main problem
   c. narration
   d. dialogue

QUIZ Unit 1 • Chapter 5 (continued)

11. Which sentence from the story is an example of narration?
    a. "I want to play with my friends."
    b. Maya's father sighed.
    c. "I have to rake the leaves."
    d. "I have an idea."

12. "It's not fair!" said Maya. Why does Maya say this?
    a. Maya has to watch her brothers again.
    b. Maya wants to have a twin sister.
    c. Maya's friend cannot come to visit.
    d. Maya had a bad day at school.

C. ➤ **Reading Strategies:** Choose the correct answer. *(16 points: 4 points each)*

13. The main idea is the _____.
    a. noun in the first sentence
    b. most important idea in a paragraph
    c. main problem of the characters
    d. information on the writer of the story

14. Details are pieces of information that help you understand the _____ of a paragraph.
    a. main idea
    b. most important opinion
    c. sentences
    d. phrases

15. Our vacation was fun and exciting. We swam in the lake and hunted for rocks. We even went fishing. What is the main idea of this paragraph?
    a. We swam in the lake.
    b. We hunted for rocks.
    c. We went fishing.
    d. Our vacation was fun and exciting.

16. Bagels are a popular breakfast food. A bagel is a type of bread. It has a hole in the middle. The underlined sentence is _____.
    a. the main idea
    b. a phrase
    c. a detail
    d. an adjective

D. ➤ **Grammar/Usage:** Choose the correct answer. *(16 points: 4 points each)*

17. The word _____ is used to describe past abilities.
    a. should
    b. will
    c. did
    d. could

18. Yesterday Juan _____ find his lost hat.
    a. don't
    b. couldn't
    c. has
    d. will

19. Chantel was full. She _____ finish her dinner.
    a. was
    b. could
    c. am
    d. couldn't

20. Before twisting his ankle, Marcus _____ run a mile.
    a. will
    b. could
    c. is
    d. should

E. ➤ **Writing** (20 points)

Writing Prompt Write a short story about a problem you worked hard to solve. Use details to support your main ideas.

TEST • Unit 1

A. ➤ Reading

The Audition

1   We had only been in America for a year when I went to my first all-state band audition. My music teacher thought I played trumpet very well. He thought I had a chance of being chosen for our state band. I was proud that he thought I might be chosen, and I respected his opinion. However, I wasn't sure I agreed with him.

My Notes

2   The other kids in school thought it was strange that I played trumpet because I was a girl. My grandfather had gotten me started. He played trumpet in a dance band when he was young. He taught me how to play after he gave me a new trumpet for my birthday. I didn't feel shy when I played with him.

3   Getting ready for the audition took a lot of work. I had to memorize a new piece of music and practice hour after hour. I had to play unfamiliar music every day, since sight reading was part of the audition. I worked so hard that my poor trumpet was begging for mercy.

4   The day of the audition I was really nervous—scared, actually. Mother tried to help. She kept saying, "Francisca, relax. You'll do fine. You always do once you get started." I was sure she was wrong.

5   When I got to the audition room, I inspected it quickly. My hands were shaking. I could feel my heart thumping. It sounded like a drum! But my mother had been right. As soon as I began to play, I was comfortable. I guess you could say my audition went as smooth as silk. I still remember my first thoughts when I got my acceptance letter. I realized the judges didn't care where I was from and that I was a girl. They just wanted to know how well I could play the trumpet.

TEST • Unit 1 (continued)

B. ➤ **Reading Comprehension:** Choose the correct answer. *(20 points: 2 points each)*

1. What instrument does Francisca play?
   a. trumpet
   b. drums
   c. flute
   d. tuba

2. For what event was Francisca practicing?
   a. playing with her grandfather
   b. playing in a dance band
   c. playing for a state band audition
   d. playing for a school band performance

3. Who encouraged Francisca to go to the audition?
   a. her mother
   b. her friends
   c. her music teacher
   d. her grandfather

4. Who got Francisca to start playing her instrument?
   a. her mother
   b. her music teacher
   c. her brother
   d. her grandfather

5. How long had Francisca lived in America?
   a. her whole life
   b. one year
   c. ten years
   d. one month

6. How did Francisca get her instrument?
   a. She saved her money to buy it.
   b. She found it at a garage sale.
   c. It was her older brother's.
   d. She received it for her birthday.

7. Some kids thought it was strange that Francisca played the trumpet because _____.
   a. she was small
   b. she was a girl
   c. she had just moved to America
   d. she was shy

8. Look at the picture of Francisca at the beginning of the reading. Which word would best describe Francisca?
   a. shy
   b. angry
   c. sad
   d. tired

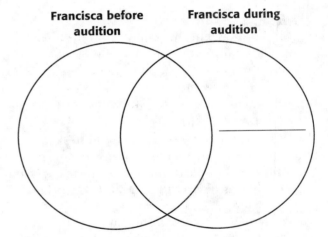

Francisca before audition   **Francisca during audition**

9. Use the Venn Diagram to compare and contrast. Which word describes how Francisca felt during the audition?
   a. comfortable
   b. nervous
   c. proud
   d. depressed

10. Based on the reading, which sentence is true?
    a. Francisca was not chosen for the band.
    b. Francisca was too nervous to perform.
    c. Francisca wrote a letter to the judges.
    d. Francisca was chosen to play in the band.

TEST • Unit 1 (continued)

C. ➤ Reading Strategies: Choose the correct answer. *(10 points: 2 points each)*

11. From paragraph 3 you can infer that
    _____.
    a. Francisca practiced once or twice a week
    b. Francisca only practiced when her mother told her to
    c. Francisca practiced every day
    d. Francisca did not practice her instrument

12. What was the effect of Francisca's practice time?
    a. She was allowed to play in her grandfather's dance band.
    b. She was given a trumpet for her birthday.
    c. She showed the judges she could play well.
    d. It made her heart beat like a drum.

13. What do you think her grandfather's reaction will be when he hears about the acceptance letter?
    a. He will take Francisca's instrument away.
    b. He will be proud of Francisca.
    c. He will quit playing his trumpet.
    d. He will practice more often.

14. Francisca was nervous on the day of her audition. What other experience might make someone feel nervous?
    a. going fishing
    b. seeing a movie with friends
    c. reading a good book
    d. entering a singing competition

15. What is the main idea of paragraph 4?
    a. Mother tried to help Francisca feel better.
    b. Mother was nervous and scared.
    c. Francisca relaxed with her mother.
    d. Francisca knew her mother was wrong.

D. ➤ Elements of Literature: Choose the correct answer. *(10 points: 2 points each)*

16. I realized the judges didn't <u>care</u> where I was from and that I was a girl. Which word rhymes with the underlined word?
    a. cart
    b. stare
    c. more
    d. candy

17. What does the phrase <u>as smooth as silk</u> in paragraph 5 tell you about Francisca's audition?
    a. It was slippery.
    b. She wore silk to the audition.
    c. The ride to the audition was not bumpy.
    d. The audition went very well.

18. I worked so hard that my trumpet was begging for mercy. Which of the following sentences has the same meaning as this sentence?
    a. I practiced really hard.
    b. I broke my trumpet.
    c. I begged for a new trumpet.
    d. I did not practice my trumpet.

19. What does paragraph 2 tell you about Francisca's grandfather?
    a. He didn't like his granddaughter.
    b. He wanted to share his love of music.
    c He didn't know how to dance.
    d. He was shy like Francisca.

20. Why did Francisca practice hour after hour?
    a. She wanted to do well at the audition.
    b. She was not good at playing the trumpet.
    c. Her teacher asked her to practice every day.
    d. She wanted to play better than her grandfather.

TEST • Unit 1 *(continued)*

E. ➤ **Vocabulary:** Choose the correct answer. *(10 points: 2 points each)*

> **well** /wɛl/ **1** *n.* a deep hole that is dug or drilled into the ground to get water, oil, or gas **2** *adv.* in a good way, skillfully

21. My music teacher thought I played trumpet very <u>well</u>. Use the dictionary entry to find a synonym for the underlined word.
    a. hole
    b. water
    c. skillfully
    d. ground

22. What does the phrase <u>sight reading</u> mean in paragraph 3?
    a. practicing music
    b. playing music for the first time
    c. memorizing music
    d. reading about eyesight

23. When I got to the audition room, I inspected it <u>quickly</u>. The word <u>quickly</u> is a(n) _____.
    a. noun
    b. adjective
    c. prefix
    d. adverb

24. I still remember my first thoughts when I got my acceptance <u>letter</u>. In this sentence <u>letter</u> means _____.
    a. to print
    b. a symbol of the alphabet
    c. an award for student athletes
    d. a written message usually sent by mail

25. My hands were shaking. I could feel my heart thumping. What do these sentences tell you about how Francisca was feeling?
    a. She was sad.
    b. She was tired.
    c. She was scared.
    d. She was in pain.

F. ➤ **Grammar/Usage:** Choose the correct answer. *(10 points: 2 points each)*

26. As soon as I opened the gift, I _____ to show my cousin.
    a. run
    b. runned
    c. ran
    d. runs

27. The movie I saw yesterday _____ great.
    a. was
    b. were
    c. be
    d. beed

28. Which sentence is written correctly?
    a. Luke practiced hard and won the race.
    b. Luke practiced hard because he won the race.
    c. So he won the race Luke practiced hard.
    d. He won the race or practiced hard.

29. Jermaine played the drums when he was young. Which phrase from the sentence is a dependent clause?
    a. Jermaine played the drums
    b. Jermaine played
    c. in a dance band
    d. when he was young

30. Her swimming lessons were a success. She _____ now swim.
    a. could
    b. will
    c. couldn't
    d. wouldn't

TEST • Unit 1 (continued)

G. ➤ Writing Conventions: Choose the correct answer. *(10 points: 2 points each)*

31. My sister likes to listen to abdullah practice the piano. Which word from the sentence should be capitalized?
    a. sister
    b. abdullah
    c. practice
    d. piano

32. I worked hard to earn the money Finally I could pay for tennis lessons. Where is a period needed?
    a. after Finally
    b. after pay
    c. after money
    d. after hard

33. This year my birthday is on a Saturday. Why is Saturday capitalized?
    a. It is the name of a day.
    b. It is the name of a month.
    c. It is the name of a country.
    d. It is the name of a person.

34. What is another way to spell the sound ou as in the word around?
    a. oo as in book
    b. oa as in boat
    c. or as in cord
    d. ow as in brown

35. What is the contraction for the words could and not?
    a. can't
    b. won't
    c. couldn't
    d. could've

H. ➤ Editing: Read and choose the correct answer. *(10 points: 2 points each)*

1 The track meet were only four days away.
2 Michael had been training for his event every day after school.
3 Running the hurdles was hard work that taked speed and powerful jumping.
4 Michael's coach said Michael was the bestest hurdler he had ever seen.
5 Michael won the race and received a blue ribbon.
6 The day of the track meet, Michael woke up rested and ready.
7 He knew his practice would pay off.
8 When the gun went off, he ran like the wind and leap like a rabbit.

36. In sentence 1, were is best written _____.
    a. was
    b. be
    c. beed
    d. as it is written

37. In sentence 3, taked is best written _____.
    a. taking
    b. takes
    c. took
    d. as it is written

38. What change should you make to sentence 4?.
    a. change *Michael's* to *Michaels*
    b. change *bestest* to *best*
    c. change *seen* to *saw*
    d. make no change

TEST • Unit 1 (continued)

39. Where does sentence 5 best fit?
  a. at the beginning of the story
  b. at the end of the story
  c. after the story's first sentence
  d. where it is

40. What change should you make to
  sentence 8?
  a. change *When* to *Where*
  b. change *he* to *she*
  c. change *leap* to *leaped*
  d. make no change

I. ➤ **Writing** *(20 points)*

> **Writing Prompt** Write a first-person
> narrative about a time when you were
> nervous or embarrassed. Tell why you
> felt that way. Explain how your feelings
> affected your actions. Use the Planning
> Guide to help you write.

Planning Guide
❏ Brainstorm ideas on a piece of paper.
❏ List details about the event you have
  chosen.
❏ Use your details to write your first-person
  narrative.
❏ Make sure that your narrative has a clear
  beginning, middle, and end.
❏ Use pronouns such as "I" and "me" in your
  narrative.

QUIZ Unit 2 • Chapter 1

A. ➤ Vocabulary: Choose the correct answer. *(24 points: 4 points each)*

1. You can use a word wheel to _____.
   a. help you remember new words
   b. finish your homework faster
   c. look up information
   d. check the spelling of words

2. The word *experiment* can be added to a word wheel for the word _____.
   a. zoo
   b. movie
   c. school
   d. science

3. _____ can be added to a word wheel for the word *holiday.*
   a. Building
   b. Celebrate
   c. Restaurant
   d. Street

4. Which word has the same beginning sound as heard in the word *father?*
   a. park
   b. pencil
   c. photo
   d. pile

5. Which word has the same ending sound as heard in the word *half?*
   a. graph
   b. that
   c. symbol
   d. phone

6. Which of these sounds do you hear in the middle of the word *symphony?*
   a. /s/
   b. /f/
   c. /h/
   d. /b/

B. ➤ Text Structure/Elements of Literature: Read and choose the correct answer. *(20 points: 4 points each)*

> "Growing and Changing"
>
> 1   Many living things change while growing. Some grow bigger. Some change colors. Others change from one living thing into another. Here is an example. A young butterfly begins its life as a type of worm. After a lot of eating and resting, it becomes a beautiful butterfly!

7. What type of reading is "Growing and Changing"?
   a. poetry
   b. fantasy
   c. first-person narrative
   d. scientific informational text

8. "Growing and Changing" tells _____.
   a. of an event in nature
   b. why things happen
   c. where living things live
   d. a made-up story about a living thing

9. What is described in this reading?
   a. why a butterfly is born
   b. how to live while growing
   c. how living things change
   d. where to find a butterfly

10. A process is _____.
   a. another name for a butterfly
   b. the order in which things happen
   c. another type of living thing
   d. a place where living things grow

11. Which sentence tells how a butterfly begins life?
   a. Some grow bigger.
   b. Some change colors.
   c. A young butterfly begins its life as a type of worm.
   d. Many living things change while growing.

QUIZ Unit 2 • Chapter 1 (continued)

C. ➤ Reading Strategies: Choose the correct answer. *(12 points: 4 points each)*

12. Ashley is reading a book titled <u>Rain, Wind, and Fog</u>. What is this book most likely about?
    a. flying kites
    b. types of weather
    c. how umbrellas are made
    d. lighthouses

13. Maribel is yawning and closing her eyes. You can infer that Maribel is _____.
    a. growing
    b. sleepy
    c. ready to play
    d. going to eat soon

14. Payton is waiting at the bus stop. You can infer that _____.
    a. Payton is waiting for a bus
    b. Payton is looking for a friend
    c. Payton is walking his dog
    d. Payton's class is going on a trip

D. ➤ Grammar/Usage: Choose the correct answer. *(24 points: 4 points each)*

15. Which verb is in the simple present tense?
    a. walking
    b. entered
    c. swim
    d. took

16. Which verb is in the simple present tense?
    a. threw
    b. sat
    c. smile
    d. clapping

17. Which verb is in the simple present tense?
    a. jumping
    b. jump
    c. jumped
    d. jumper

18. Which sentence shows simple present tense?
    a. We drove to the store.
    b. Tyrone used my pencil.
    c. Mother works in that building.
    d. I took the test.

19. Which sentence shows simple present tense?
    a. They ride all over town.
    b. He cooked the turkey.
    c. I read that book yesterday.
    d. Will Jana be joining us?

20. Which sentence shows simple present tense?
    a. You eat the pizza.
    b. He drank my milk.
    c. Shoveling snow was hard work.
    d. My hands shook from fright.

E. ➤ Writing *(20 points)*

Writing Prompt Write a paragraph about something you have learned about in science class. Use information you have learned to describe or explain your science topic.

QUIZ Unit 2 • Chapter 2

A. ➤ Vocabulary: Choose the correct answer. *(28 points: 4 points each)*

1. I <u>flew</u> down the stairs to answer the door. In this sentence, <u>flew</u> means _____.
   a. crawled
   b. ran
   c. walked
   d. tiptoed

2. "This is the best day of my life!" Maria <u>cried</u>. Which word means nearly the same as <u>cried</u>?
   a. shouted
   b. whispered
   c. sang
   d. mumbled

3. The summer <u>showers</u> cooled the hot air. Which word means nearly the same as <u>showers</u>?
   a. bath
   b. party
   c. rain
   d. sunshine

4. We <u>consumed</u> every crumb of food on the table. Which word means nearly the same as <u>consumed</u>?
   a. threw away
   b. saved
   c. cooked
   d. ate

5. The suffix *-ty* means _____.
   a. to look for a number
   b. to do something again
   c. tens or times tens
   d. time on a clock

6. What smaller word do you see in the word <u>seventy</u>?
   a. six
   b. seven
   c. eight
   d. nine

7. What is another way to write 40?
   a. twenty
   b. thirty
   c. forty
   d. fifty

B. ➤ Text Structure/Elements of Literature: Read and choose the correct answer. *(16 points: 4 points each)*

"The Most Important Job"

July 4, 1776

1   Papa told me to wait by the door, outside Independence Hall. Congress was meeting inside. They were deciding if the colonies should be free from Britain. What if the answer was yes? I would have to run to tell Papa to ring the bell.

2   Papa often lets me go with him to ring the bell. He says he remembers the day the bell was delivered from London. It was 25 years ago. He was about my age then and his papa was the bell ringer.

3   As soon as the doorkeeper said the Declaration of Independence was accepted, I ran to Papa. "Ring, ring, ring the bell for independence!" I cried. And Papa let me help him pull the rope.

8. This is an example of part of a _____.
   a. historical fiction diary
   b. third-person narrative
   c. poem
   d. play

9. What is the date of the entry?
   a July 4, 2000
   b. April 19, 1976
   c. July 4, 1776
   d. June 3, 2002

QUIZ Unit 2 • Chapter 2 *(continued)*

10. Which event really happened?
    a. The Declaration of Independence was signed.
    b. Papa was at Independence Hall.
    c. The boy ran home.
    d. The boy helped ring the bell.

11. He says he remembers the day the bell was delivered from London, 25 years before. This sentence is an example of _____.
    a. setting   c. vocabulary
    b. dialogue   d. flashback

C. ➤ Reading Strategies: Choose the correct answer. *(16 points: 4 points each)*

12. When you summarize, you _____.
    a. read quickly
    b. look for mistakes in each sentence
    c. tell about the most important information
    d. make predictions

13. The most important information in a paragraph is usually found in the _____.
    a. first and last sentences
    b. title of the story
    c. middle of the paragraph
    d. dialogue of the story

14. It was a great day for Quentin. He was first in line for the shower. He had his favorite breakfast. Which of these summarizes the sentences?
    a. Quentin was in a bad mood.
    b. Quentin ate breakfast.
    c. Quentin needed something.
    d. Quentin had a good day.

15. The kinds of dogs you can choose for a pet are amazing. They come in all sizes and colors. Which of these summarizes the sentences?
    a. There are many types of dogs.
    b. Small dogs make good pets.
    c. Pets are amazing animals.
    d. Colorful dogs are the best.

D. ➤ Grammar/Usage: Choose the correct answer. *(20 points: 4 points each)*

16. We _____ the test tomorrow.
    a. took
    b. taked
    c. will took
    d. will take

17. Victor _____ in the race.
    a. will run
    b. runned
    c. will ran
    d. will runs

18. The neighbors _____ our fish while we're away.
    a. was watching
    b. will watch
    c. watches
    d. is watching

19. After dinner, I _____ my homework.
    a. will did
    b. will done
    c. does
    d. will do

20. Next year, my sister _____ to high school.
    a. went
    b. goes
    c. will go
    d. had gone

E. ➤ Writing *(20 points)*

Writing Prompt Write your own diary entry. Use today's date. Write about real people and real events that are happening in your life.

QUIZ Unit 2 • Chapter 3

A. ➤ Vocabulary: Choose the correct answer. *(24 points: 4 points each)*

1. The LINK strategy stands for **L**ist, **I**nquire, **N**ote, and _____.
   a. **K**eep
   b. **K**now
   c. **K**een
   d. **K**ick

2. Aston wants to create a LINK chart for the word <u>obstacle</u>. What should she do for the "L" section of the chart?
   a. listen to her friends talk about obstacles
   b. look up *obstacle* in the dictionary
   c. list all the words she can think of that relate to obstacles
   d. learn how to navigate an obstacle course

3. Which sentence can be completed with the word <u>it's</u>?
   a. _____ a cold, rainy day.
   b. The cow found ___ calf.
   c. _____ page is torn.
   d. Summer is pleasant with _____ warm days.

4. Which sentence can be completed with the word <u>its</u>?
   a. I can't come, because _____ too late.
   b. _____ my turn.
   c. _____ the nicest letter I've ever read.
   d. The snake shed _____ skin.

5. The house needed to have _____ roof fixed.
   a. that's
   b. it's
   c. they're
   d. its

6. December is my favorite month. _____ when we visit relatives.
   a. Of
   b. Its
   c. Is not
   d. It's

B. ➤ Text Structure/Elements of Literature: Read and choose the correct answer. *(24 points: 4 points each)*

"A New Life"

Scene 2

1 FRAN: It won't be that bad. You'll see.

2 LISA: Not that bad? (*She flops down on the bed and hugs a pillow to her chest.*) It's going to change everything! Life as I know it is over. Poof! Gone!

3 FRAN: (*rummaging through the closet, holding clothes up as if trying them on*) I think it's kind of cool. Your mom's having a baby! That's exciting news. You'll be a big sister.

4 LISA: Yeah, but I'm used to it just being me. I like having this room to myself.

7. Lisa and Fran are the _____.
   a. setting
   b. characters
   c. scene
   d. narrator

8. "A New Life" is part of a _____.
   a. play
   b. novel
   c. diary
   d. letter

9. This dialogue takes place during _____.
   a. scene 1
   b. scene 2
   c. act 1
   d. act 2

10. Who is Fran?
   a. the narrator
   b. the director
   c. Lisa's friend
   d. Lisa's sister

11. Where does this scene take place?
    a. on the bus
    b. in the living room
    c. at school
    d. in Lisa's room

12. Which of these props is needed for the scene?
    a. a backpack
    b. a pillow
    c. a telephone
    d. books

C. ➤ Reading Strategies: Choose the correct answer: (16 points: 4 points each)

13. The order in which events happen is the _____.
    a. plot
    b. setting
    c. sequence of events
    d. details

14. Which of these events happened first?
    a. We tried to eat the oatmeal, but it was too hot.
    b. Mother made oatmeal for breakfast.
    c. We returned from the garage and ate the oatmeal.
    d. We cleaned the garage while the oatmeal cooled.

15. Which of these events happened last?
    a. Then we planted the seeds.
    b. Finally, we watered the garden.
    c. We tilled the soil.
    d. First we cleared the area of stones and twigs.

16. Sasha stopped at the bakery. She bought something to eat. She finished it and threw away her napkin. What happened after Sasha finished eating?
    a. She stopped at the bakery.
    b. She bought something to eat.
    c. She ate something from the bakery.
    d. She threw away her napkin.

D. ➤ Grammar/Usage: Choose the correct answer. (16 points: 4 points each)

17. Which sentence shows the future conditional?
    a. Nan will clean her room on Saturday.
    b. If Jose studies, he will do well on the test.
    c. I don't know if I can come.
    d. Will you call me tomorrow?

18. Which sentence shows the future conditional?
    a. If I eat that, I will be sick.
    b. Is it okay if I go too?
    c. What time is it?
    d. I can go there next week.

19. If I use my umbrella, _____.
    a. I needed to stay dry
    b. I will stay dry
    c. I doesn't get wet
    d. it was cold

20. _____, I will be hungry later.
    a. If I eat now
    b. When I ate yesterday
    c. If I ate tomorrow
    d. If I eat last month

E. ➤ Writing (20 points)

Writing Prompt Write a scene for a play. Think of a favorite story. Choose part of the story when two characters are talking to each other.

VISIONS B Assessment Program • Copyright © Heinle

QUIZ Unit 2 • Chapter 4

A. ➤ Vocabulary: Choose the correct answer. *(32 points: 4 points each)*

1. <u>Teacher</u>, <u>books</u>, <u>students</u>, <u>learn</u>, and <u>homework</u> are all related to the word _____.
   a. home
   b. bank
   c. library
   d. school

2. <u>Pool</u>, <u>suit</u>, and <u>towel</u> are all related to the word _____.
   a. swimming
   b. jogging
   c. entertainment
   d. exercise

3. <u>Lunch</u>, <u>menu</u>, <u>waitress</u>, and <u>order</u> are all related to the word _____.
   a. museum
   b. grocery store
   c. restaurant
   d. airport

4. Which word is related to <u>hospital</u>?
   a. fire truck
   b. zebra
   c. doctor
   d. teeth

5. Which word is related to <u>city</u>?
   a. country
   b. building
   c. farm
   d. mountain

6. There was no hope for fixing the car. The situation was _____.
   a. hopeless
   b. helpful
   c. fixable
   d. careless

7. After running, Sonny was out of breath. Sonny was _____.
   a. breathing
   b. runner
   c. careless
   d. breathless

8. Kayla was not careful with the glass. She was _____.
   a. hopeless
   b. careful
   c. helping
   d. careless

B. ➤ Text Structure/Elements of Literature: Read and choose the correct answer. *(16 points: 4 points each)*

> "The Accident"
>
> 1 My brother, Alejandro, fell off of his bike. He twisted his ankle. My parents took him to see the doctor. The doctor said it would be a long time before his ankle felt better. A long time.
>
> 2 I tried to make Alejandro more comfortable. I rearranged his room. I put the things that he liked most close to his bed. Alejandro smiled when he saw what I did for him.

9. What type of writing has made-up events that could happen in real life?
   a. nonfiction
   b. narratives
   c. realistic fiction
   d. fantasy

10. "The Accident" is a _____.
    a. diary entry
    b. first-person narrative
    c. poem
    d. play

11. Some writers use incomplete sentences _____.
    a. because they haven't learned writing rules
    b. to save space
    c. to better express themselves
    d. because they write fiction

QUIZ Unit 2 • Chapter 4 (continued)

12. In paragraph 1, why does the author use the incomplete sentence "A long time"?
   a. to save space
   b. to help readers practice reading those words
   c. to show excitement
   d. to stress that Alejandro would not be walking anytime soon

C. ➤ Reading Strategies: Choose the correct answer. *(16 points: 4 points each)*

13. In order to draw a conclusion, you must think carefully about all of the _____.
   a. opinions
   b. wishes
   c. stories
   d. facts

14. It is dark outside. I know that the sun does not go down before 6 P.M. Therefore, I can conclude that _____.
   a. it is before 6 P.M.
   b. it is autumn
   c. it is morning
   d. it is after 6:00 P.M.

15. Delmar is wearing a hat, gloves, and a heavy coat. He is also wearing boots. You can conclude that _____.
   a. it is warm outside
   b. it is hot outside
   c. it is cold outside
   d. it is raining outside

16. Antonio and Tara have the same parents. You can conclude that _____.
   a. their parents are at home
   b. their parents are nice
   c. Antonio and Tara are friends
   d. Antonio and Tara are brother and sister

D. ➤ Grammar/Usage: Choose the correct answer. *(16 points: 4 points each)*

17. I could not wait to lie on the soft pillow. Which word from the sentence is the adjective?
   a. I
   b. wait
   c. soft
   d. pillow

18. I searched up and down the crowded beach for my friends. Which word from the sentence is the adjective?
   a. searched
   b. crowded
   c. beach
   d. friends

19. My doctor made me take the dreadful medicine every day. What word does dreadful describe?
   a. doctor
   b. me
   c. take
   d. medicine

20. Reading five chapters is an enormous homework assignment. What word does the adjective enormous describe?
   a. reading
   b. five
   c. chapters
   d. assignment

E. ➤ Writing *(20 points)*

> **Writing Prompt** Write a realistic story about a family who faced a challenge. Tell how the challenge changed the family.

QUIZ Unit 2 • Chapter 5

A. ➤ Vocabulary: Choose the correct answer. *(24 points: 4 points each)*

1. Your <u>payment</u> is due. What is the root word of <u>payment</u>?
   a. ent
   b. ay
   c. ment
   d. pay

2. They <u>traveled</u> west. What is the root word of <u>traveled</u>?
   a. travel
   b. tra
   c. led
   d. veled

3. Which word contains the root word <u>wonder</u>?
   a. warm
   b. wonderful
   c. won
   d. watchful

4. Which word contains the root word <u>delight</u>?
   a. doing
   b. depressing
   c. delightful
   d. dark

5. The state of being happy is called _____.
   a. healthy
   b. happiness
   c. happy
   d. helpful

6. The state of being dark is called _____.
   a. darkness
   b. day
   c. darker
   d. noon

B. ➤ Text Structure/Elements of Literature: Read and choose the correct answer. *(20 points: 4 points each)*

"On the Oregon Trail"

June 17, 1847

1   We lost the Adams' wagon today. The wheel broke at the shaft. We have no more parts to spare. We have now lost 14 wagons on this journey. The others will carry what they can of the Adams' belongings. Folks are now walking alongside the remaining wagons. They walk with others whose wagons are buried in the past. This Oregon Trail has robbed the smiles from every face. The men no longer speak of the possibilities before them.

---

7. How is a journal different from a diary?
   a. A journal is written by adults.
   b. A journal is written for others to read.
   c. Journals do not talk about daily experiences.
   d. Journals are always about Native Americans.

8. Which event happened first?
   a. The wagon wheel broke.
   b. The wagons set out on the Oregon Trail.
   c. They ran out of food.
   d. They had 100 miles left to travel.

9. A/an _____ is a way of describing something by showing its similarity to something else.
   a. metaphor
   b. antonym
   c. multiple meaning word
   d. process

10. This Oregon Trail has robbed the smiles from every face. What does this sentence from the reading mean?
    a. Thieves were on the trail.
    b. Someone stole the smiles.
    c. No one was smiling.
    d. Everyone was robbed.

QUIZ Unit 2 • Chapter 5 (continued)

11. They walk with others <u>whose wagons are buried in the past.</u> What does the underlined phrase mean?
    a. They buried the broken wagons.
    b. The wagons needed to be buried.
    c. There were shovels in the wagons.
    d. The wagons were left behind.

C. ➤ Reading Strategies: Choose the correct answer. *(16 points: 4 points each)*

12. Which event would be first on a timeline?
    a. someone's first day in first grade
    b. learning to drive
    c. someone's first job
    d. graduating from high school

13. Which event would be last on a timeline?
    a. Abraham Lincoln was elected president.
    b. Texas became the 28th state.
    c. The pilgrims sailed to America.
    d. George W. Bush was elected president.

14. Which dates are in the correct order?
    a. 1482, 1840, 1804, 1812
    b. 1840, 1482, 1812, 1804
    c. 1804, 1482, 1840, 1812
    d. 1482, 1804, 1812, 1840

15. George Washington was born on February 22, 1732. He married Martha Custis in January 1759. He became the first president of the United States in 1789. What event took place in 1759?
    a. George Washington was born.
    b. George Washington became our nation's first president.
    c. George Washington left the United States.
    d. George Washington married Martha Custis.

D. ➤ Grammar/Usage: Choose the correct answer. *(20 points: 4 points each)*

16. Which sentence shows the present continuous tense?
    a. He went to bed.
    b. We are eating dinner.
    c. They will not be able to make it.
    d. She did not call me.

17. Which sentence shows the present continuous tense?
    a. He looked tired.
    b. My stomach is growling.
    c. We can go later.
    d. Please leave a message.

18. Which sentence shows the present continuous tense?
    a. They will have to hurry.
    b. She did not hurry, so she was late.
    c. They hurried out the door.
    d. I am trying to hurry.

19. My boss _____ vacationing. Use the present continuous tense to finish the sentence.
    a. was
    b. went
    c. is
    d. will go

20. They _____ very loud. Use the present continuous tense to finish the sentence.
    a. can be
    b. are being
    c. were
    d. will be

E. ➤ Writing *(20 points)*

> **Writing Prompt** Think about an event you have learned about in history or social studies. Write a journal entry as if you are taking part in that event. Use metaphors in your writing.

TEST • Unit 2

A. ➤ Reading

Escaping the Dust Bowl

1　August 16, 1934

　　I don't think we'll ever make it to California! For weeks we have been on this road with thousands of other cars and trucks. We are like ants scurrying for food. It seems so long ago that we left Oklahoma, driven out by the dust storms that always blew our crops away. No matter how hard we worked, the yellowish-brown haze would appear on the horizon, swallowing up everything in its path.

2　　It didn't matter that we had no money. No rain and poor soil make farming futile. When people from the bank started to come, Pa said it was time to go. We had no money for food, let alone to pay the bank. We heard stories about people threatening bankers with guns and pitchforks. Frightening stories. They did almost anything to get the bankers off the land. In the end, the banks always won, and Pa did not want to risk our safety. He saw flyers that claimed California needed farmers. We packed up everything that we could fit in the truck and left.

My Notes

3　August 18, 1934

　　We finally made it! It is so beautiful. Everywhere we look we see rolling hills full of crops. Many people tell us there is no work, but Pa is confident. He says if we look hard enough, we will find work soon.

4　August 22, 1934

　　Still no work to be found. Everywhere we look, thousands of people just like us are trying to get the same handful of jobs. Not only is there no work, but the residents we see tell us they don't want us here. They tell us to go back home. Pa says there is no turning back now. We have nothing to go back to.

TEST • Unit 2 (continued)

B. ➤ Reading Comprehension: Choose the correct answer. *(20 points: 2 points each)*

1. In paragraph 1, where is the family traveling?
   a. California
   b. Oklahoma
   c. the horizon
   d. an ant farm

2. In paragraph 1, how long has the family been traveling?
   a. a year
   b. many months
   c. many weeks
   d. a few days

3. Why did the family leave their home?
   a. They were driven out by floods.
   b. The dust storms made farming difficult.
   c. Ants killed the crops.
   d. They could not breathe in the dust.

4. Who came to take farms away from the owners?
   a. other farmers
   b. ranchers
   c. bankers
   d. fruit companies

5. Why do you think the farms were taken away?
   a. The people were bad farmers.
   b. The farmers lost a bet.
   c. The farmers had too much land.
   d. The farmers could not pay their bills.

6. How was the family traveling?
   a. by car
   b. by truck
   c. by boat
   d. by train

7. When did the family reach its destination?
   a. August 16, 1934
   b. August 18, 1934
   c. August 22, 1934
   d. August 15, 1934

8. In paragraph 3, what are people saying?
   a. They do not know how to dream.
   b. They can see hills full of crops.
   c. They all have jobs.
   d. There are no jobs.

9. In paragraph 3, Pa seems _____.
   a. angry
   b. determined
   c. scared
   d. nervous

10. In paragraph 4, why is the writer sad?
    a. She is homesick for her old farm.
    b. There are thousands of people around her.
    c. The people she meets do not want her family around.
    d. Pa says they will go back home.

VISIONS B Assessment Program • Copyright © Heinle

TEST • Unit 2 *(continued)*

C. ➤ Reading Strategies: Choose the correct answer. *(10 points: 2 points each)*

11. We can infer from paragraph 2 that _____.
    a. Pa got in a fight with the bankers
    b. some farmers became angry with the bankers
    c. Pa already had a job out West
    d. the farmers did not help each other

12. Which sentence best summarizes paragraph 4?
    a. Things are not working out well, but the family cannot go back.
    b. Mean people will not give the family jobs, so they will go somewhere else.
    c. Thousands of people live in the town.
    d. The writer wants to go home.

13. Which event from the reading happened after Pa saw flyers advertising work?
    a. They packed the truck and left.
    b. The bankers took all of the farms.
    c. Dust storms blew the crops away.
    d. They worked hard to save the farm.

14. Pa did not want to risk our safety. We can conclude from this sentence that _____.
    a. Pa was angry with his family
    b. Pa was a risk taker
    c. Pa loved his family
    d. Pa had hidden money from the bankers

15. When did the family leave home?
    a. on August 16, 1934
    b. before August 16, 1934
    c. after August 16, 1934
    d. August 18, 1934

D. ➤ Elements of Literature: *(10 points: 2 points each)*

16. Paragraph 2 is an example of _____.
    a. symbolism
    b. future tense
    c. sequence
    d. flashback

17. What is the setting for paragraph 1?
    a. at home on the farm
    b. somewhere along the road
    c. at the bank
    d. on hills full of crops

18. They did almost anything to get the bankers off the land. This sentence from paragraph 2 shows that _____.
    a. the farmers and bankers lived on the same land
    b. the farmers and bankers fought over who would have the land
    c. other people sold the farmers' land to bankers
    d. the writer thought banks were located on all of the land

19. Frightening stories. This line from the reading shows which style of writing?
    a. flashback
    b. metaphor
    c. past tense words
    d. an incomplete sentence

20. In paragraph 4, what does handful of jobs mean?
    a. There were jobs in which you work with your hands.
    b. There were many jobs.
    c. There were very few jobs.
    d. There were jobs for anyone who raised their hands.

TEST • Unit 2 (continued)

E. ➤ Vocabulary: Choose the correct answer. *(10 points: 2 points each)*

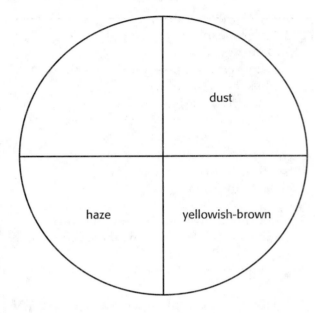

21. Which word from the reading should be added to the word wheel above?
   a. farms
   b. dust storms
   c. jobs
   d. crops

22. No rain and poor soil make farming futile. Futile means _____.
   a. impossible
   b. profitable
   c. fun
   d. exciting

23. It is so beautiful. What is another way to write this sentence from the reading?
   a. It am so beautiful.
   b. It's so beautiful.
   c. Is it so beautiful?
   d. Its is so beautiful.

24. In this reading, the words rain, soil, produce, and crops all relate to _____.
   a. bankers
   b. dust storms
   c. finding work
   d. farming

25. We finally made it! What is the root word of finally?
   a. finish
   b. fin
   c. ly
   d. final

F. ➤ Grammar/Usage: Choose the correct answer. *(10 points: 2 points each)*

26. Which of these phrases is in the simple present tense?
   a. we had no money
   b. we heard stories
   c. we see rolling hills
   d. he saw flyers

27. Which of these phrases is in the future tense?
   a. we have been on this long road
   b. we left Oklahoma
   c. it didn't matter
   d. we will find work

28. Which of these phrases is a future conditional?
   a. if we look hard enough, we will find work soon
   b. go back home
   c. the banks always won
   d. haze would appear

29. No rain and poor soil make farming futile. What does the adjective poor describe?
   a. rain
   b. soil
   c. farming
   d. the farmers

TEST • Unit 2 *(continued)*

30. Which of these phrases is in the present continuous tense?
   a. thousands of people are trying to get the same handful of jobs
   b. the banks always won
   c. we packed up everything
   d. haze would appear

G. ➤ Writing Conventions: Choose the correct answer. *(10 points: 2 points each)*

31. Which word has the same beginning sound as <u>kite</u>?
   a. city
   b. photo
   c. chemical
   d. cells

32. Which is the correct way to write <u>24</u>?
   a. twent and four
   b. twentie four
   c. twenty-four
   d. twenty, fore

33. I don't think we'll ever make it to <u>California</u>! Why is <u>California</u> capitalized?
   a. It is the author's name.
   b. It is a month.
   c. It is at the beginning of a sentence.
   d. It is the name of a state.

34. We _____ to go swimming. Which spelling correctly completes the sentence?
   a. dessided
   b. decided
   c. dasidet
   d. deesided

35. Which word has the same ending sound as <u>comb</u>?
   a. count
   b. fawn
   c. soon
   d. same

H. Editing: Read and choose the correct answer. *(10 points: 2 points each)*

> 1 My grandpa lived during the Great Depression.
> 2 He <u>telled</u> me those <u>was</u> the hardest times he has ever lived through.
> 3 Grandpa said that sometimes they didn't have none money for weeks and weeks.
> 4 His family works hard to take care of each other.
> 5 Now Grandpa reminds us to be thankful for all that we have.

36. In sentence 1, <u>telled</u> is best written _____.
   a. did tells
   b. tell
   c. told
   d. as it is written

37. In sentence 2, <u>was</u> is best written _____.
   a. were
   b. are
   c. will
   d. as it is written

38. What change should you make to sentence 3?
   a. change *they* to *them*
   b. change *none* to *any*
   c. change *for* to *because*
   d. make no change

39. What change should you make to sentence 4?
   a. change *His* to *Her*
   b. change *family* to *family's*
   c. change *works* to *worked*
   d. make no change

40. What change should you make to sentence 5?
   a. change *reminds* to *remind*
   b. change *us* to *we*
   c. change *have* to *has*
   d. make no change

TEST • Unit 2 *(continued)*

I. Writing *(20 points)*

> **Writing Prompt** Write a scientific informational text about a living thing that changes in nature. Describe the living thing. Write about how it changes during a process. Use the Planning Guide to help you.

Planning Guide
- ❑ Brainstorm living things from nature on a piece of paper.
- ❑ Choose a living thing to write about.
- ❑ List details about the living thing that you chose.
- ❑ Write ideas about how the process changes the living thing you chose.
- ❑ Use your details and ideas to write your informational text.

VISIONS B Assessment Program • Copyright © Heinle

QUIZ Unit 3 • Chapter 1

A. ➤ **Vocabulary:** Choose the correct answer. *(24 points: 4 points each)*

1. The pronunciation key in a dictionary helps you to _____.
   a. learn how to say new words
   b. learn what a new word means
   c. find synonyms of unknown words
   d. learn how to use the new word in a sentence

2. Contractions make sentences _____.
   a. shorter
   b. longer
   c. easier to describe
   d. harder to understand

3. Contractions always include a(n) _____.
   a. pronoun
   b. complete sentence
   c. form of the verb <u>to be</u>
   d. apostrophe

4. Juanita couldn't play outside until she finished her homework. Which word is the contraction?
   a. outside
   b. play
   c. chores
   d. couldn't

5. Luis and Lupe <u>do not</u> like to take the bus. What is another way to write the phrase <u>do not</u>?
   a. can't
   b. don't
   c. shouldn't
   d. didn't

6. _____ is a contraction.
   a. She'll
   b. He played
   c. You will
   d. She may

B. ➤ **Text Structure/Elements of Literature:** Read and choose the correct answer. *(24 points: 4 points each)*

> "Puppy Love"
>
> 1 Puppies may be brown or black,
>   White or maybe gray.
>   They love to get attention
>   As they romp around and play.
>   They love to get attention
>   Every single night and day!

7. "Puppy Love" is a _____.
   a. realistic adventure
   b. personal narrative
   c. poem
   d. fable

8. Which line from the poem is an example of repetition?
   a. Puppies may be brown or black,
   b. White or maybe gray.
   c. As they romp around and play.
   d. They love to get attention

9. Which two words in the poem rhyme?
   a. single/night
   b. brown/black
   c. gray/play
   d. love/day

10. The poem has _____ stanza(s).
    a. one
    b. two
    c. three
    d. four

11. In "Puppy Love," <u>play</u> and <u>day</u> are examples of _____.
    a. exact rhyme
    b. similar rhyme
    c. synonyms
    d. proper nouns

QUIZ Unit 3 • Chapter 1 (continued)

12. Which two words are an example of similar rhyme?
    a. strong/length
    b. crib/bib
    c. feared/disappeared
    d. hungry/angry

C. ➤ Reading Strategies: Choose the correct answer. *(12 points: 4 points each)*

13. The feathers floated in the wind. This sentence best helps you to picture the feathers as _____.
    a. soft and light
    b. heavy and round
    c. shiny and colorful
    d. wet and big

14. Enrique shouted and stomped his feet. This sentence helps you to picture Enrique as _____.
    a. happy
    b. angry
    c. grateful
    d. loving

15. Which of the following sentences creates a strong image in your mind?
    a. I left for school on time.
    b. Lightning lit up the black sky as the rain came pounding down.
    c. My favorite after-school sport is baseball.
    d. I read a very good book yesterday.

D. ➤ Grammar/Usage: Choose the correct answer. *(20 points: 4 points each)*

16. A prepositional phrase _____.
    a. always begins the sentence
    b. always includes a pronoun
    c. always ends the sentence
    d. gives you more information

17. A prepositional phrase has of a(n) _____.
    a. pronoun and a noun
    b. object and a name
    c. noun and a verb
    d. preposition and an object

18. Pedro played the tuba in the school band. What question does the prepositional phrase in the band answer?
    a. how Pedro played
    b. who played with Pedro
    c. where Pedro played
    d. when Pedro went to school

19. Esteban left his shoes under the bed. Under is a _____.
    a. noun
    b. preposition
    c. verb
    d. pronoun

20. Louisa is saving money in the bank. What is the prepositional phrase in this sentence?
    a. is saving
    b. saving money
    c. in the bank
    d. Louisa is

E. ➤ Writing *(20 points)*

Writing Prompt Write a poem that describes something you feared in the past. Write about how you felt.

VISIONS QUIZ Unit 3 • Chapter 1

VISIONS B Assessment Program • Copyright © Heinle

QUIZ Unit 3 • Chapter 2

A. ➤ Vocabulary: Choose the correct answer. *(32 points: 4 points each)*

1. Synonyms are words that _____.
   a. have opposite meanings
   b. sound the same
   c. are spelled the same
   d. have similar meanings

2. The best source to use to find a synonym is a(n) _____.
   a. thesaurus
   b. rhyming dictionary
   c. encyclopedia
   d. map

3. Jaime received <u>excellent</u> grades. _____ is a synonym for <u>excellent</u>.
   a. Normal
   b. Very good
   c. The same
   d. Very poor

4. Andrea is <u>scared</u> of science fiction movies. _____ is a synonym for <u>scared</u>.
   a. Tired
   b. Happy
   c. Afraid
   d. Proud

5. Alejandro grabbed his book to <u>prevent</u> it from falling. _____ is a synonym for <u>prevent</u>.
   a. Stop
   b. Point
   c. Hide
   d. Divide

6. My friend, Alonzo, is a good student. The word Alonzo is capitalized because it is _____.
   a. the first word in the sentence
   b. easier to read
   c. the name of a place
   d. a proper noun

7. Dallas is an important city in texas. Which word in the sentence should be capitalized?
   a. texas
   b. important
   c. city
   d. an

8. A person from California is called a _____.
   a. California
   b. Californie
   c. Callie
   d. Californian

B. ➤ Text Structure/Elements of Literature: Read and choose the correct answer. *(24 points: 4 points each)*

"Sacajawea"

1   Sacajawea was a Shoshone Indian. She was born about 1790. In 1804, she began serving as a guide for Lewis and Clark. She led them through dangerous territory. Lewis and Clark became famous American explorers. Sacajawea's picture is on a special one-dollar coin.

---

9. "Sacajawea," is an example of _____.
   a. realistic adventure fiction
   b. a personal narrative
   c. a poem
   d. a biography

10. Which should be included in a biography?
   a. a myth about the person
   b. a play about the life of the person
   c. important dates in the person's life
   d. a poem about the person

VISIONS QUIZ Unit 3 • Chapter 1

QUIZ Unit 3 • Chapter 2 (continued)

11. _____ are important or special things that happened in Sacajawea's life.
    a. dates
    b. events
    c. descriptions
    d. titles

12. How was Sacajewea important to Lewis and Clark?
    a. She was their mother.
    b. She served as a guide for them.
    c. She showed them how to make coins.
    d. She helped them to get their pictures on the dollar.

13. The phrase In 1804 is a _____.
    a. transition
    b. proper noun
    c. synonym
    d. contraction

14. "Sacajawea" is written in _____.
    a. reverse order
    b. stanzas
    c. chronological order
    d. complex sentences

C. ➤ Reading Strategies: Choose the correct answer. (12 points: 4 points each)

15. _____ are the most important parts of a story.
    a. Main ideas
    b. Supporting details
    c. Causes and effects
    d. Clauses

16. José felt sick. He had a headache and a bad cough. His mother made him stay at home to rest. What is the main idea of this story?
    a. José felt sick.
    b. José decided to play outside.
    c. José wanted to stay home.
    d. José did not do his homework.

17. Tatiana saw flashing lights and fire engines. She knew there was an emergency. What are the supporting details in this story?
    a. Tatiana caused an emergency while she was home.
    b. Tatiana saw flashing lights and fire engines
    c. Tatiana was curious.
    d. There was an emergency.

D. ➤ Grammar/Usage: Choose the correct answer. (12 points: 4 points each)

18. Two-word verbs are used to _____.
    a. point out adjectives
    b. describe a meaning
    c. explain an action
    d. show a place in the story

19. Everett left after his sister did, but he _____ with her quickly.
    a. caught up
    b. looked around
    c. studied
    d. was alone

20. Lorenzo left out an important ingredient in the cake. Left out is a _____.
    a. simile
    b. two-word verb
    c. prepositional phrase
    d. proper noun

E. ➤ Writing (20 points)

> **Writing Prompt** Write a short biography about someone you know. Use chronological order and transitions in your biography.

VISIONS B Assessment Program • Copyright © Heinle

QUIZ Unit 3 • Chapter 3

A. ➤ Vocabulary: Choose the correct answer. *(24 points: 4 points each)*

1. Using <u>context clues</u> means _____.
   - **a.** studying contractions and their meanings
   - **b.** studying the first and last words in sentences
   - **c.** studying nearby words and meanings
   - **d.** studying nouns and pronouns in sentences

2. Carlos always hid his catcher's glove. His <u>valuables</u> were important to him. In this sentence, <u>valuables</u> means _____.
   - **a.** something the owner doesn't like
   - **b.** something special to the owner
   - **c.** something that is easily lost
   - **d.** something to play with

3. Esperanza tried out for the team three years in a row. <u>Finally</u>, she made it! In this sentence <u>finally</u> means _____.
   - **a.** at last
   - **b.** on the first try
   - **c.** the last one to try out
   - **d.** the first one to leave

4. Adding *-ion* to the end of a verb often changes it to a(n) _____.
   - **a.** pronoun
   - **b.** noun
   - **c.** adjective
   - **d.** adverb

5. In the word <u>instruction</u>, the *ion* is a(n) _____.
   - **a.** prefix
   - **b.** suffix
   - **c.** synonym
   - **d.** antonym

6. Which of the following becomes a new word when *-ion* is added?
   - **a.** secure
   - **b.** invent
   - **c.** equip
   - **d.** settle

B. ➤ Text Structure/Elements of Literature: Read and choose the correct answer. *(24 points: 4 points each)*

> "My Terrible Day"
>
> Dear Diary,
>
> 1   Today was such a bad day! I overslept and got to school late. I forgot my library books. Then I only got a 75 on my spelling test! Mom gave me a bologna sandwich for lunch, and I hate bologna! I did not study very much for the science test. Some of the questions were so hard! On the way home from school, Rosa and I had a fight. I am glad this day is over!

7. "My Terrible Day," is an example of _____.
   - **a.** realistic adventure fiction
   - **b.** biography
   - **c.** a poem
   - **d.** a diary entry

8. A diary is a _____.
   - **a.** true story about transportation
   - **b.** personal record of life events
   - **c.** fictional story
   - **d.** short story

9. Diaries often have a(n) _____ writing style.
   - **a.** adventurous
   - **b.** sad
   - **c.** informal
   - **d.** formal

10. The feeling that a writer shows when writing is called _____.
    - **a.** tone
    - **b.** plot
    - **c.** moral
    - **d.** dialogue

QUIZ Unit 3 • Chapter 3 (continued)

11. What is the tone of "My Terrible Day?"
   a. lazy
   b. tired
   c. frustrated
   d. happy

12. "I will find him no matter what," said Pepe when his dog disappeared. What is the tone of this sentence?
   a. happy
   b. funny
   c. serious
   d. cheerful

C. ➤ Reading Strategies: Choose the correct answer. *(12 points: 4 points each)*

13. _____ tell(s) us the order in which things happen.
   a. Chronology
   b. Conjunctions
   c. Prepositions
   d. Main ideas

14. Alonzo studied on Thursday. He took his test on Friday. He rested on Saturday. What did Alonzo do the day before he rested?
   a. studied
   b. took a test
   c. slept
   d. rested some more

15. Esteban lived in Smallville for three years. Then, he moved to Goldtown for one year, and then to Woodhaven for two months. Finally, he moved to Sandpiper six months ago. Where did Esteban live last?
   a. Goldtown
   b. Smallville
   c. Sandpiper
   d. Woodhaven

D. ➤ Grammar/Usage: Choose the correct answer. *(20 points: 4 points each)*

16. _____ join two sentences.
   a. Conjunctions
   b. Suffixes
   c. Root words
   d. Contractions

17. Leonardo wanted to go with his friends, but he did not finish his homework. Which word is a conjunction in the sentence?
   a. friends
   b. wanted
   c. but
   d. did

18. Maria watched television for an hour, and then her mother told her to go outside. Which word is a conjunction in the sentence?
   a. and
   b. outside
   c. mother
   d. watched

19. Carlos went to visit his grandmother, _____ he was only able to stay for two days. Which word best completes the sentence?
   a. so   c. but
   b. since   d. thus

20. Horatio needed to practice the piano, <u>but</u> he wanted to play ball. <u>But</u> is used to show _____ in the sentence.
   a. differences
   b. length
   c. contrast
   d. connections

E. ➤ Writing *(20 points)*

Writing Prompt Write a diary entry describing a recent day in your life. Use conjunctions to form compound sentences.

QUIZ Unit 3 • Chapter 4

A. ➤ **Vocabulary:** Choose the correct answer. *(24 points: 4 points each)*

1. A reference aid is a _____.
   a. source of information
   b. place for medicine
   c. source of food
   d. place for books

2. Which of these is an example of a reference aid?
   a. pencil
   b. scratch paper
   c. marker
   d. Internet

3. _____ make(s) writing more colorful and exciting!
   a. Figurative language
   b. Context clues
   c. Capitals
   d. Synonyms

4. Hector thought the <u>sun rose and set</u> with his baby brother. He loved him very much. Hector most likely meant that his brother was _____.
   a. very special to him
   b. usually away on trips
   c. difficult to talk to
   d. outside a lot

5. Maria and her sister were very close. Friends said the two were <u>joined at the hip</u>. This means Maria and her sister were _____.
   a. always fighting
   b. always together
   c. shared the same room
   d. almost the same age

6. Alejandro vowed to <u>give it his all</u> to win the game. This means he would _____.
   a. go to meetings
   b. take time off
   c. work very hard
   d. show up every day

B. ➤ **Text Structure/Elements of Literature:** Read and choose the correct answer. *(24 points: 4 points each)*

> "Hailing a Hero"
>
> 1 We are here today to honor an outstanding person. He is a firefighter who risks his life every day. Last week, he risked his life for two small children. Horatio and Pilar are alive today because of his actions. Pedro Garcia, please stand up. We salute you!

7. "Hailing a Hero" is an example of a _____.
   a. realistic adventure fiction
   b. speech
   c. poem
   d. diary entry

8. "Hailing a Hero" is written for a(n) _____.
   a. another speaker
   b. play
   c. writer
   d. audience

9. Style, tone, and mood are _____.
   a. the same thing
   b. not important
   c. tools for writers
   d. used only in poetry

10. Luis felt that it was all right to stay up past bedtime. His parents did not agree. The tone of this story is _____.
    a. approving
    b. disapproving
    c. puzzling
    d. funny

QUIZ Unit 3 • Chapter 4 *(continued)*

11. The tree branches screeched as they brushed against the broken window. The wind howled in the night. A shadow moved across the lawn. The mood of this story is _____.
    a. happy
    b. sad
    c. angry
    d. scary

12. Ernesto always put his studies first. He felt they would lead him to a successful future. The style of this story is _____.
    a. tone
    b. angry
    c. formal
    d. informal

C. ➤ Reading Strategies: Choose the correct answer. *(12 points: 4 points each)*

13. Opinions can change, but a fact can be _____.
    a. proven
    b. false
    c. bought
    d. fiction

14. "Miguel is the nicest boy in the class," said Rosa. Rosa's statement is a(n) _____.
    a. fact
    b. opinion
    c. question
    d. guess

15. Father bought tickets for the 3:00 P.M. train. This sentence is an example of a(n) _____.
    a. fact
    b. opinion
    c. guess
    d. hope

D. ➤ Grammar/Usage: Choose the correct answer. *(20 points: 4 points each)*

16. Pedro has many chores. Pedro prefers making his bed. It is the _____ for him.
    a. easiest
    b. easy
    c. easier
    d. most easy

17. A superlative adjective always _____.
    a. ends in er
    b. ends in ing
    c. compares at least three things
    d. uses most at least three times

18. The three dogs are all big. But Manuela's dog is the _____.
    a. biggest
    b. bigger
    c. better
    d. big

19. Bernardo, Lorenzo, and Hector play sports four days per week. It's hard to decide who is the _____.
    a. activer
    b. activist
    c. most active
    d. acting

20. Erica and Ernesto are strong, but Manuel is the _____.
    a. most strongest
    b. strongest
    c. less strongest
    d. most strong

E. ➤ Writing *(20 points)*

Writing Prompt Write a speech introducing someone you know and admire. Describe why he or she should be honored. Use superlative adjectives to help describe the person that you choose.

QUIZ Unit 3 • Chapter 5

A. ➤ Vocabulary: Choose the correct answer. *(24 points: 4 points each)*

1. The students <u>bellow</u> across the playground to each other. In this sentence, <u>bellow</u> means _____.
   a. safe
   b. shout
   c. whisper
   d. play

2. Lorenzo's dog <u>whines</u> when she wants to come inside. In this sentence, <u>whines</u> means to _____.
   a. give a long, soft, high cry
   b. laugh without stopping
   c. try something again
   d. run around in circles

3. Horatio raced <u>frantically</u> to the bus stop but still missed the bus. <u>Frantically</u> means _____.
   a. going slowly
   b. in a rushed way
   c. moving backwards
   d. walking in a straight line

4. The definition of <u>lighthouse</u> can be figured out by separating it into _____.
   a. consonants
   b. two words
   c. vowels
   d. prefixes

5. Which of the following is a compound word?
   a. bedroom
   b. wallpaper
   c. overboard
   d. all of the above

6. <u>Bookmark</u> is made up of the words _____.
   a. <u>boom</u> and <u>mark</u>
   b. <u>boo</u> and <u>book</u>
   c. <u>book</u> and <u>mark</u>
   d. <u>booker</u> and <u>marking</u>

B. ➤ Text Structure/Elements of Literature: Read and choose the correct answer. *(24 points: 4 points each)*

> "Remembering Grandpa"
>
> 1   When I was a little girl, I spent special time with my grandpa. I went with him to work. I was able to see how he helped put books together. It was so exciting to touch the huge stacks of colored paper. I could smell the paper and glue as he worked. I will never forget those days, and I will certainly never forget Grandpa.

7. "Remembering Grandpa" is an example of a _____.
   a. realistic adventure fiction
   b. memoir
   c. poem
   d. biography

8. "Remembering Grandpa" focuses on _____.
   a. remembering special people and events
   b. the history of humor
   c. how something came to be
   d. how an audience responds to stories

9. A memoir might describe _____.
   a. how plants make food
   b. how to play a game
   c. a job you would like
   d. your best kindergarten friend

10. Pedro wanted to be a hero. He never realized how much courage he would need. Soon his courage would be put to the test. This story shows _____.
    a. foreshadowing
    b. compound words
    c. synonyms
    d. figurative language

QUIZ Unit 3 • Chapter 5 (continued)

11. A bolt of lightening flashed across the night sky. Maria shuddered as the wind grew stronger. What is probably being foreshadowed here?
    a. Maria's going to get lost.
    b. It's going to rain.
    c. Maria has no way to get home.
    d. The weather will clear tomorrow.

12. By the end of the semester, Carlos would learn the true meaning of friendship. This sentence most likely means that _____.
    a. Carlos was going to fail a class
    b. Carlos would learn about friendship
    c. Carlos would learn about science
    d. Carlos was going to have a bad semester

C. ➤ Reading Strategies: Choose the correct answer. *(12 points: 4 points each)*

13. Emmanuel wants to be just like his big brother. Emmanuel is thus probably _____ than his brother.
    a. older
    b. younger
    c. stronger
    d. smarter

14. Ming's mother and father were out. Ming decided to set the table for her family. She put five plates on the table. Ming is most likely _____.
    a. looking for something to do
    b. listening to music
    c. preparing for dinner
    d. babysitting for a neighbor

15. Phillip is waiting for his school bus to come to school. What is most likely the time of day?
    a. early morning
    b. dinner time
    c. afternoon
    d. late at night

D. ➤ Grammar/Usage: Choose the correct answer. *(20 points: 4 points each)*

16. Pronouns are used in place of _____.
    a. adjectives
    b. adverbs
    c. commas
    d. nouns

17. Jayna is very polite. <u>She</u> always places her napkin in her lap. <u>She</u> stands for _____.
    a. manners
    b. Jayna
    c. lap
    d. napkin

18. All the teachers attended the meeting, and then <u>they</u> discussed student grades. <u>They</u> stands for_____.
    a. all the teachers
    b. the meeting
    c. student grades
    d. the school

19. <u>Fernando, Luiz, and I</u> met at school and decided what we would do afterwards. The word _____ refers to <u>Fernando, Luiz, and I</u>.
    a. I
    b. we
    c. met
    d. would

20. LaToya and her sisters went to school together. <u>They</u> all had to be there at 8:30 A.M. <u>They</u> refers to _____.
    a. school
    b. LaToya
    c. home
    d. LaToya and her sisters

E. ➤ Writing (20 points)

Writing Prompt Write a memoir. Choose a meaningful person or event in your life to describe.

Grade

TEST • Unit 3

A. ➤ Reading

The Girl Named Anne

My Notes

1   Anneliesse Marie Frank was born in Frankfurt, Germany on June 12, 1929. Her parents were Otto and Edith Frank. Her older sister was named Margot. The family was very happy in Germany. However, when Anne was four, the Franks moved to Holland. They moved because a political

group called the Nazis was terrorizing Jewish people like the Franks. They made people like Anne and her family find places where they would be safe. While living in Holland, Anne's parents built a hiding place, which was a group of rooms right above her father's office.

2   Anne had received her diary about a month before they went into hiding and used it to write down her thoughts and feelings about everything. In her diary, Anne wrote about what it was like to live with her family in the hiding place. Although the hiding space was small, Anne and her family felt safe there. They felt lucky that they were together. Although Anne and her family were always afraid that the Nazis would find them, they still did the same things that other families.

3   Unfortunately, Anne and her sister could not always do things that were fun. They had to be very quiet since they lived above her father's office. They did not want anyone to discover their hiding place. So, when Anne got bored, she read books, listened to the radio, and wrote in her diary. She shared her feelings about growing up and about being afraid of what was happening to her and her family.

4   Anne and her family's worst fears eventually came true. They were discovered by the Nazis and sent to prison camps. Sadly, Anne died in a camp. After she died, her father published her diary. He wanted everyone to know about the girl named Anne.

TEST • Unit 3 (continued)

B. ➤ Reading Comprehension: Choose the correct answer. *(20 points: 2 points each)*

1. "The Girl Named Anne" is a(n) _____.
   a. biography
   b. interview
   c. poem
   d. speech

2. "The Girl Named Anne" tells about _____.
   a. the history of the world
   b. a person's life
   c. how Germany became a country
   d. how to write a personal story

3. "The Girl Named Anne" is mostly about _____.
   a. Germany
   b. the president
   c. Anne Frank
   d. the United States

4. Anne wrote her thoughts _____.
   a. on a computer
   b. in a diary
   c. on the radio
   d. in a textbook

5. What is a diary?
   a. a movie about something
   b. a picture of a family
   c. a poem about feelings
   d. a record of a person's thoughts

6. Anne Frank had a sister named Margot. This is an example of a(n) _____.
   a. opinion
   b. fact
   c. dialogue
   d. quote

7. At the end of the story, Anne's father_____.
   a. writes a story of his own
   b. finds his wife
   c. publishes Anne's diary
   d. moves to New York City

8. Why does Anne write in her diary?
   a. to keep a safety record
   b. to write poems about friendship
   c. to talk to her sister
   d. to explore her thoughts and feelings

9. In paragraphs 1 and 2, how does Anne's family feel about being together?
   a. sleepy
   b. happy
   c. lately
   d. funny

10. What does the tone of this story tell the reader?
    a. Anne Frank is an important historical figure
    b. biographies are funny
    c. the Nazis were afraid
    d. Anne's real name was Anneliesse

VISIONS B Assessment Program • Copyright © Heinle

TEST • Unit 3 (continued)

C. ➤ Reading Strategies: Choose the correct answer. *(10 points: 2 points each)*

11. In "The Girl Named Anne," what is the main idea of paragraph 3?
    a. Anne could not always do fun things in hiding.
    b. Anne liked to go many places.
    c. Margot shared her feelings with Anne.
    d. Otto Frank had an office near Anne's hiding place.

12. What happened after Anne's family moved to Holland?
    a. They went back to Frankfurt.
    b. They built a hiding place.
    c. Anne was born.
    d. Margot was born.

13. "The Girl Named Anne" is based on _____.
    a. what Anne feels
    b. what others think
    c. opinions
    d. facts

14. You can best conclude that Anne Frank was _____.
    a. happy
    b. tired
    c. brave
    d. sleepy

15. Which sentence supports that Anne's and her family's fear came true?
    a. Anne Frank was born in Frankfurt, Germany on June 12, 1929.
    b. They were discovered by the Nazis and sent to prison camps.
    c. They did not want anyone to discover their hiding place.
    d. Anne and her family felt safe there.

D. ➤ Elements of Literature: Choose the correct answer. *(10 points: 2 points each)*

16. "The Girl Named Anne" tells about the life of Anne Frank using _____.
    a. a play
    b. reverse order
    c. chronological order
    d. a speech

17. So when Anne got bored, she read <u>books</u>. Which word rhymes with <u>books</u>?
    a. sees
    b. looks
    c. finds
    d. shops

18. What is the tone of "The Girl Named Anne?"
    a. happy
    b. funny
    c. amusing
    d. serious

19. The style of "The Girl Named Anne" is _____.
    a. formal
    b. casual
    c. courage
    d. happy

20. In paragraph 1, Anne used her diary to write down her thoughts and feelings. The writer tells this to _____.
    a. show that Anne was a good writer
    b. foreshadow the publishing of Anne's diary
    c. prepare the reader for Anne's move
    d. give away the ending to the story

VISIONS TEST Unit 3

TEST • Unit 3 (continued)

E. ➤ Vocabulary: Choose the correct answer. *(10 points: 2 points each)*

21. They were <u>discovered</u> by the Nazis. A synonym for <u>discovered</u> is _____.
   a. found
   b. taken
   c. hidden
   d. kept

22. Anne and her sister couldn't always do things that were fun. Which word in the sentence is a contraction?
   a. her
   b. couldn't
   c. always
   d. were

23. However, when Anne was four, the Franks moved to Holland. Holland is capitalized because it _____.
   a. should begin the sentence
   b. is the name of a person
   c. is the name of a country
   d. is at the end of the sentence

24. A(n) _____ is a reference book that includes synonyms for words.
   a. encyclopedia
   b. thesaurus
   c. map
   d. Internet

25. Where could you look to find out how to pronounce the word <u>Nazis</u>?
   a. a dictionary
   b. an encyclopedia
   c. synonym finder
   d. in the story

F. ➤ Grammar/Usage: Choose the correct answer. *(12 points: 4 points each)*

26. Anne wrote about what it was like to live in the hiding place. What is the prepositional phrase in the sentence?
   a. Anne wrote
   b. what it was like
   c. to live
   d. in the hiding place

27. Which is an example of a two-word verb?
   a. Margot will
   b. write down
   c. walked quickly
   d. safe place

28. They were scared, but they still tried to have fun. What is the conjunction in the sentence?
   a. they
   b. were
   c. but
   d. to

29. Anne had to be the <u>quietest</u> during the day. Quietest is a(n) _____.
   a. action word
   b. superlative adjective
   c. pronoun
   d. comparative adjective

30. That book is great! It is about an adventure. *It* stands for _____.
   a. that
   b. that book
   c. great
   d. an adventure

TEST • Unit 3 (continued)

G. ➤ Writing Conventions: *(10 points: 2 points each)*

31. "_____ a beautiful day outside," she replied. Which word correctly completes the sentence?
    a. is
    b. its
    c. is'
    d. It's

32. Vivian would like to go _____. Which word correctly completes the sentence?
    a. too
    b. two
    c. to
    d. teo

33. Which book title is capitalized correctly?
    a. angelo's baking disaster
    b. Angelo's baking disaster
    c. Angelo's Baking Disaster
    d. angelo's Baking disaster

34. The poem was titled, Winter in the Mountains. What should be added to the sentence?
    a. quotations around the word poem
    b. quotation marks around the words Winter in the Mountains
    c. an apostrophe after the word Winter
    d. a question mark at the end of the sentence

35. Which of these correctly shows the beginning of a letter?
    a. dear Papa,
    b. DEAR PAPA,
    c. dear papa,
    d. Dear Papa,

H. ➤ Editing: *(10 points: 2 points each)*

> **Malik's Day**
>
> 1 Malik awoke early on Saturday.
> 2 He was <u>look</u> forward to playing soccer with his friends.
> 3 He got dressed and ran downstairs to get breakfist.
> 4 His father was making pancakes.
> 5 Him mother was reading the newspaper.
> 6 Malik was feeling good so he looked outside.
> 7 It was pouring rain.
> 8 Malik sighed or waited patiently for his turn to read the morning paper.

36. In sentence 1, <u>look</u> is best written _____.
    a. lookest
    b. looker
    c. looking
    d. as it is written

37. What change should you make to sentence 3?
    a. change *go* to *get*
    b. change *and* to *but*
    c. change *breakfist* to *breakfast*
    d. make no change

38. What change should you make to sentence 5?
    a. change *Him* to *His*
    b. change *reading* to *read*
    c. change the period to a question mark at the end of the sentence
    d. make no change

39. What change should you make to sentence 6?
    a. change *feeling* to *feel*
    b. change *so* to *until*
    c. change the period to a question mark at the end of the sentence
    d. make no change

TEST • Unit 3 (continued)

40. What change should you make to
sentence 8?
   a. change *or* to *and*
   b. change *patiently* to *patient*
   c. change *read* to *reading*
   d. make no change

I. ➤ Writing *(20 points)*

> **Writing Prompt** Write a biography
> about someone you know who shows
> courage. Use the Planning Guide to help
> you write.

Planning Guide
❏ Choose someone you know that shows
  courage.
❏ Write ways that this person has shown
  courage in his or her life.
❏ Write your biography using the
  information from above.
❏ Use chronological order in your
  biography.
❏ When you have finished, proofread your
  biography for correct punctuation,
  spelling, and grammar.

MID-BOOK EXAM

A. ➤ Reading

The Changing Ice

My Notes

1   Antarctica is the highest, driest, windiest, coldest place on Earth. Anyone who visits this white continent will certainly agree with that.

2   Antarctica's ice holds 70 percent of Earth's fresh water. As the ocean freezes in winter, the continent actually doubles in size. Ice forms at the incredible rate of 2.2 miles per minute.

> **Come take a virtual tour of ANTARCTICA**
>
> Now showing at the Museum of Science Wonders 11:00 and 3:00 daily
>
> Admission is Free!

3   All of this ice comes from two processes. In the first process, ice breaks apart and spreads. Giant ice shelves extend from the continent out over the ocean. When ocean waves swell, large sections of the shelves break off and form icebergs. These icebergs have straight sides and flat tops, like a table. As a result, they are called "tabular" icebergs. As they float in the ocean, wind and water erode their edges, both above and below the surface of the sea. This causes the icebergs to break into smaller pieces. Pieces that are about the size of a house are known as "bergy bits." Wind and waves cause the bergy bits to roll over. Magical shapes that were carved under water are revealed. Bergy bits break into even smaller pieces. Pieces that are about the size of a car are called "growlers." They get their name from the sound they make as they scrape along the sides of ships. The ice continues to break down. In the end, the sea is covered by small, slushy pieces of ice known as "brash ice."

4   In the second process, new ice is created. As winter approaches, a thin skin of "frazil ice" forms on the ocean's surface. When these ice crystals collect, the water has a greasy look. This is called "grease ice." The layer of grease ice continues to thicken. Ocean waves create round-shaped ice with curled edges known as "pancake ice." Finally, these pancakes are pushed together by waves and form the "fast" ice that encloses Antarctica for its long, cold winter.

MID-BOOK EXAM (continued)

Ice Cold Ice

<table>
<tr><td></td><td>

1 There are tabular icebergs
   And icebergs that growl,
   Fast ice and sea ice—
   I can't keep track of them all.

2 Frazil ice, grease ice, and
   Bergy bits are ice, too.
   Some ice is white,
   Some is incredibly blue.

3 Ice shaped like pancakes
   Has edges that curl
   As the sea freezes over
   And cold winter winds swirl.

4 But "fraziled" or "bergy,"
   They're a sight to behold,
   And I do know for certain
   Each one is quite cold!

</td><td>**My Notes**</td></tr>
</table>

B. ➤ Reading Comprehension: Choose the correct answer. *(20 points: 2 points each)*

1. How much of Earth's fresh water is found in Antarctica's ice?
   a. 2.2 square miles of it
   b. 23 square miles of it
   c. 70 percent of it
   d. all of it

2. What causes the formation of tabular icebergs?
   a. ice shelves breaking apart
   b. wind
   c. frazil ice
   d. ships scraping along side of them

3. How much larger does Antarctica get in the winter?
   a. It gets 23 times larger.
   b. It gets 75 times larger.
   c. It becomes twice as large.
   d. It becomes 2.2 times larger.

4. What is the biggest size iceberg?
   a. growlers
   b. pancake ice
   c. bergy bits
   d. tabular icebergs

5. What is the thin skin of ice that forms on the ocean around Antarctica in winter?
   a. bergy bits
   b. frazil ice
   c. brash ice
   d. greasy ice

6. How big are growlers?
   a. hundreds of feet high
   b. the size of a house
   c. the size of a dog
   d. the size of a car

7. What is the highest continent in the world?
   a. North America
   b. Asia
   c. Europe
   d. Antarctica

MID-BOOK EXAM (continued)

8. What type of ice has curled edges?
   a. frazil ice
   b. brash ice
   c. pancake ice
   d. fast ice

9. What causes ice shelves to break off?
   a. wind erosion
   b. ocean swells
   c. ships passing by
   d. a drop in temperature

10. What kind of ice encloses Antarctica for the winter?
   a. fast ice
   b. pancake ice
   c. brash ice
   d. growlers

C. ➤ Reading Strategies: Choose the correct answer. *(10 points: 2 points each)*

11. How are the poem and the science text alike?
   a. They both rhyme.
   b. They both tell about different kinds of ice.
   c. They both give information about the size of icebergs.
   d. They both tell about how ice is formed.

12. What is the main idea of "The Changing Ice?"
   a. Antarctica is cold.
   b. Antarctica has huge tabular icebergs.
   c. Antarctica has many different types of ice.
   d. Antarctica's ice holds about 70 percent of the world's fresh water.

13. Which of the following statements is an opinion?
   a. All the ice is a sight to behold.
   b. The thin skin of ice is called "frazil ice."
   c. "Pancake ice" is pushed together by waves.
   d. Antarctica is the highest, driest, windiest, coldest place on the Earth.

14. As winter approaches, a thin skin of "frazil ice" forms on the surface of the ocean. What can you infer from this sentence from "The Changing Ice?"
   a. The temperature is rising.
   b. The temperature continues to be cold.
   c. The temperature drops below freezing.
   d. The temperature does not change.

15. Magical shapes that were carved under water are revealed. This statement from "The Changing Ice" helps the reader picture the ice as _____.
   a. cold
   b. different colors
   c. beautiful
   d. soft

D. ➤ Text Structure/Elements of Literature: Choose the correct answer. *(10 points)*

16. Which phrase from the readings gives an example of personification?
   a. the ocean waves swell
   b. icebergs that growl
   c. are called tabular icebergs
   d. is known as grease ice

17. Which words show an example of an exact rhyme?
   a. growl/all
   b. ice/white
   c. behold/cold
   d. icebergs/ice

18. Which phrase uses a simile to describe ice?
   a. some ice is white
   b. has edges that curl
   c. They're a sight to behold
   d. Ice shaped like pancakes

MID-BOOK EXAM (continued)

19. Which paragraph in "The Changing Ice" shows the cycles of large pieces of ice being changed into smaller pieces of ice?
 a. paragraph 1
 b. paragraph 2
 c. paragraph 3
 d. paragraph 4

20. How would you describe the style of "Ice Cold Ice"?
 a. serious
 b. formal
 c. angry
 d. informal

E. ➤ Vocabulary: Choose the correct answer. *(10 points: 2 points each)*

21. Some icebergs are incredibly blue. Which word is a synonym for incredibly?
 a. pretty
 b. unbelievably
 c. doubtfully
 d. possibly

22. Icebergs are a sight to behold. Behold means _____.
 a. see
 b. dislike
 c. teach
 d. hold

23. A thin skin of frazil ice forms on the ocean's surface. Which word could be used instead of skin?
 a. piece
 b. hide
 c. peeling
 d. layer

24. "Wind and waves cause the bergy bits to roll over. Magical shapes that were carved under water are revealed." Using context, you know that the word revealed probably means _____.
 a. shown
 b. hidden
 c. colored
 d. destroyed

25. Fake, fence, find, _____, friendly. Which word completes the alphabetical list?
 a. finance
 b. frizzy
 c. frontier
 d. frazil

F. ➤ Grammar/Usage: Choose the correct answer. *(10 points: 2 points each)*

26. Which sentence shows the past tense of the verb be?
 a. All of this ice will be the result of two processes.
 b. All of this ice could be the result of two processes.
 c. All of this ice would result from two processes.
 d. All of this ice was the result of two processes.

27. Which sentence has a dependent clause?
 a. As the ocean waves swell, large sections of the shelves break off.
 b. I can't keep track of them all.
 c. Frazil ice, grease ice, and bergy bits are ice, too.
 d. This is called "grease ice."

MID-BOOK EXAM (continued)

28. Which sentence is in the future tense?
   a. In the second process, new ice is created.
   b. This causes the icebergs to break into smaller pieces.
   c. Anyone who visits this white continent will certainly agree with that.
   d. These ice shelves are hundreds of feet high.

29. Which phrase has an adjective before the noun?
   a. when cold winter winds swirl
   b. continues to break down
   c. ice continues to thicken
   d. this causes the icebergs to break

30. Which sentence has a prepositional phrase?
   a. Anyone who visits this white continent will certainly agree.
   b. As they float in the ocean, wind and water erode these edges.
   c. This is called "grease ice."
   d. Finally, these pancakes are pushed together.

G. ➤ Writing Mechanics: Choose the correct answer. *(10 points: 2 points each)*

31. Which sentence is capitalized correctly?
   a. I go to the Movies on saturday.
   b. Every Monday, Macy goes shopping.
   c. we eat pepperoni pizza every tuesday.
   d. Tabular ice is Beautiful.

32. Which sentence shows the correct use of quotation marks?
   a. "Antarctica, the white continent, is covered with ice.
   b. "I want to go to Antarctica," said Lois.
   c. The whale was enormous."
   d. That's "amazing!

33. Which sentence uses apostrophes correctly?
   a. The oceans surface was covered with frazil ice.
   b. Some children built a snow fort'.
   c. The ocean's surface was as smooth as glass.
   d. Our lunch start's at noon.

34. In which sentence is the suffix *-less* added correctly to the underlined word?
   a. Luisa sighed <u>unhappyless</u>.
   b. Wei-Lin thought she could <u>waitless</u> no longer.
   c. Marco was getting <u>tiredless</u> as he worked.
   d. The puppy's energy seemed <u>endless</u>.

35. Which sentence uses hyphens correctly?
   a. Thirty one penguins jumped onto the iceberg.
   b. Thirty-one penguins jumped onto the iceberg.
   c. Thirty one penguins jumped on-to the iceberg.
   d. Thirty-one penguins-jumped-onto the iceberg.

MID-BOOK EXAM *(continued)*

H. ➤ **Editing:** Read and choose the correct answer. *(10 points: 2 points each)*

Frazil Ice

1 Frazil ice is a very thin layer of ice on the ocean.
2 It is made from ice crystals.
3 These crystals are formed as deep as thirty-two feet down.
4 They float to the surface.
5 Here they join together to make frazil ice.
6 It looks like ice needles.
7 This is an amazing process.

---

36. Which of the following rewrites sentence 3 in the simple present tense?
   a. Ice crystals formed deep below the surface.
   b. Deep below the surface many ice crystals were formed.
   c. Ice crystals form thirty-two feet below the surface.
   d. Ice crystals will form deep below the surface.

37. How can you rewrite sentence 3 using a superlative adjective?
   a. The deepest these crystals form is thirty-two feet down.
   b. The most deepest these crystals form is thirty-two feet down.
   c. These crystals are formed as deepest as thirty-two feet down.
   d. These crystals are formed as deeper as thirty-two feet down.

38. In sentence 4, the pronoun they refers to _____.
   a. the ocean
   b. frazil ice
   c. ice crystals
   d. waves

39. Which of the following rewrites sentence 4 in the past tense?
   a. They could float to the surface.
   b. They will float to the surface.
   c. They floated to the surface.
   d. Ice floats to the surface.

40. Which of the following uses a dependent clause to combine sentences 4 and 5?
   a. They float to the surface and make frazil ice.
   b. When they float to the surface, they make frazil ice.
   c. Ice crystals make frazil ice.
   d. Ice crystals float to the surface.

I. ➤ **Writing** *(20 points)*

Writing Prompt Write a five-paragraph realistic adventure story about a challenge a character faces. Tell how the character changes as a result of the challenge. Use the Planning Guide to help you write.

Planning Guide
❑ Be sure your story has a beginning, a middle, and an end.
❑ Describe the challenge.
❑ Explain how the challenge is met.
❑ Explain how the character is changed by the challenge.
❑ Write neatly.

VISIONS B Assessment Program • Copyright © Heinle

Grade

QUIZ Unit 4 • Chapter 1

A. ➤ Vocabulary: Choose the correct answer. *(24 points: 4 points each)*

1. _____ is when writers say the same thing more than once.
   a. Synonym
   b. Repetition
   c. The definition
   d. The adjective

2. The silly feeling <u>vanished</u>. Which word can replace the underlined word?
   a. moved
   b. returned
   c. disappeared
   d. cried

3. She was <u>whirling</u> around until she became dizzy. Which word can replace the underlined word?
   a. walking
   b. spinning
   c. leaning
   d. sitting

4. That bug is a <u>cicada</u>. Which word means the same as <u>cicada</u>?
   a. worm
   b. bird
   c. mongoose
   d. seventeen-year locust

5. The man's favorite season is <u>autumn</u>. Which word means the same as <u>autumn</u>?
   a. salt
   b. fall
   c. trip
   d. winter

6. The <u>employer</u> gave each worker a gift. Which word means the same as <u>employer</u>?
   a. boss
   b. student
   c. worker
   d. job

B. ➤ Text Structure/Elements of Literature: Read and choose the correct answer. *(28 points: 4 points each)*

"The Class Project"

1   Ms. Smith is helping her class finish their yearly art projects. Last year, the students' art was shown only at the school. This year, the students' art will be displayed at the local library. The students are excited. They will walk to the library to take their art.

---

7. "The Class Project" is _____.
   a. a biography
   b. fiction
   c. a poem
   d. a myth

8. Ms. Smith is _____.
   a. part of the setting of the story
   b. the plot of the story
   c. one of the characters in the story
   d. the person who makes up the story

9. Which of these events happened first in the story?
   a. The students are excited.
   b. The students' art is displayed at the library.
   c. Ms. Smith helps her class finish their art projects.
   d. The students walk to the library.

"The Wonders of Nature"

1 Just around the corner, not far from where I stay

2 I see the wonders of nature each and every day.

3 And I hear the sounds of nature as I listen to the whisper of the lake

4 And I feel the touch of nature with each green grass that I take.

QUIZ Unit 4 • Chapter 1 (continued)

10. _____ is the way writers use language to express themselves.
   a. style
   b. pictures
   c. comparison
   d. synonym

11. Why is the word <u>and</u> used in line 3 of "The Wonders of Nature"?
   a. to show compound sentences
   b. to separate harder words
   c. to make the poem longer
   d. to show there is more to tell

12. The words <u>and I hear the sound of nature</u> in line 3 refer to _____.
   a. the speaker whispering to the lake
   b. the speaker listening to the lake
   c. the lake being very big
   d. the lake being quiet

13. Line 4 of the poem tells you more about the speaker by letting you know _____.
   a. the speaker likes the color green
   b. the grass is touching the speaker
   c. the speaker likes to lay on the grass
   d. the speaker takes the grass to feel it

C. ➤ Reading Strategies: Choose the correct answer. *(16 points: 4 points each)*

14. To _____ is to see how two or more things are the same.
   a. compare
   b. contrast
   c. write
   d. read

15. To _____ is to see how two or more things are different.
   a. compare
   b. contrast
   c. write
   d. read

16. The big fish lives in water. The long eel lives in water. How can you compare the fish and the eel?
   a. They are both big.
   b. They both live in water.
   c. They are both long.
   d. The fish is big, but the eel is long.

17. The gray rhino is big. The gray bird is small. How can you contrast the bird and the rhino?
   a. The bird is tall, but the rhino is short.
   b. The bird and the rhino are animals.
   c. The rhino is big, but the bird is small
   d. The bird is gray, but the rhino is not.

D. ➤ Grammar/Usage: Choose the correct answer. *(12 points: 4 points each)*

18. A _____ is a group of words that has a subject and a verb.
   a. clause   c. suffix
   b. pronoun   d. prefix

19. Luisa looked for the key that she had lost. What is the relative clause in the sentence?
   a. Luisa looked
   b. for the
   c. that she had lost
   d. Luisa's key she had

20. He sat under the big tree that is in the park. What is the relative clause in the sentence?
   a. He sat under
   b. under the tree
   c. the tree that is
   d. that is in the park

E. ➤ Writing *(20 points)*

Writing Prompt Write a fictional paragraph about something that has been discovered. Use relative clauses.

QUIZ Unit 4 • Chapter 2

A. ➤ **Vocabulary:** Choose the correct answer. *(20 points: 4 points each)*

1. _____ are the most important words in a narrative.
   a. Describing words
   b. Proper nouns
   c. Big phrases
   d. Key words

2. The <u>volcano</u> erupted on the other side of the island. Which word from the sentence is related to the word <u>volcano</u>?
   a. erupted
   b. of
   c. other
   d. side

3. Which word is the past tense of <u>rally</u>?
   a. rallyed
   b. rallied
   c. ralied
   d. rallyd

4. Which word is the past tense of <u>slip</u>?
   a. slipeed
   b. slap
   c. slopd
   d. slipped

5. Which word is the past tense of <u>describe</u>?
   a. describing
   b. scribor
   c. described
   d. scribe

B. ➤ **Text Structure/Elements of Literature:** Read and choose the correct answer. *(28 points: 4 points each)*

"The Island of Oahu"

1   I went on vacation to Oahu, Hawaii. My friends Michelle and Tanya went with me. We did many things in Oahu. We watched the dolphins swim in the ocean. We saw huge volcanoes and mountains. One island activity included a mountain climb. But I was afraid to participate. I stayed behind while Michelle and Tanya climbed the mountain. My friends said that it was the best thrill of their lives. For me, the thrill was seeing the beauty of the island of Oahu.

---

6. "The Island of Oahu" is told from _____.
   a. third-person point of view
   b. first-person point of view
   c. Michelle's point of view
   d. the reader's point of view

7. The narrator of this story can also be called the _____ of the story.
   a. teller
   b. listener
   c. reader
   d. plot

8. The words <u>I</u>, <u>we</u>, and <u>me</u> are called _____.
   a. nouns
   b. adjectives
   c. verbs
   d. pronouns

9. Where did the speaker of this story travel?
   a. to a nature garden
   b. to a friend's home
   c. to the island of Oahu
   d. to a mountain

QUIZ Unit 4 • Chapter 2 (continued)

10. Which sentence from the story tells that the speaker was scared to climb the mountain?
    a. But I was afraid to participate.
    b. We watched the dolphins swim in the ocean.
    c. We saw huge volcanoes and mountains.
    d. One island activity included a mountain climb.

11. Why did the narrator go to the island?
    a. to meet other family members
    b. for a school trip
    c. to attend a meeting
    d. for vacation

12. You can tell that "The Island of Oahu" is a nonfiction narrative because it _____.
    a. uses dates to tell a story
    b. describes real events as they happened
    c. uses three people to tell a funny story
    d. begins and ends in Hawaii

C. ➤ Reading Strategies: Choose the correct answer. (16 points: 4 points each)

13. Graphic information can help you _____.
    a. look at the pictures
    b. figure out the meaning of adjectives
    c. understand a reading
    d. find characters in a reading

14. You can use graphics to _____.
    a. locate and learn information
    b. describe the tone of a story
    c. count the number of pronouns in a story
    d. tell the main idea of a story

15. Graphic sources of information consist of _____.
    a. verbs, maps, and adjectives
    b. pictures, maps, and timelines
    c. a main idea and a conflict
    d. a story and a plot

1970	1980	1985
Hawaii's population is 769,913	Hawaii's population is 964,691	Hawaii's population is 1,054,000

16. What does the timeline tell you about Hawaii's population?
    a. Between 1970 and 1985 Hawaii's population did not change.
    b. In 1985 Hawaii's population decreased.
    c. Hawaii's population increased between 1970 and 1985.
    d. Hawaii is a place that people love to visit.

D. ➤ Grammar/Usage: Choose the correct answer. (16 points: 4 points each)

17. An infinitive is the word _____ followed by the simple form of a verb.
    a. it   c. are
    b. we   d. to

18. The speaker is difficult to hear. Which word from the sentence is a form of the verb be?
    a. speaker   c. difficult
    b. is   d. hear

19. Which sentence uses a form of the verb be?
    a. Stay inside of the house.
    b. It was impossible to see.
    c. Do not stop there.
    d. Go to the front of the line.

20. The cookies were easy to make. The word easy is a(n)____.
    a. adjective   c. verb
    b. noun   d. adverb

E. ➤ Writing (20 points)

> **Writing Prompt** Write a nonfiction narrative about a place that you like to visit. Use first-person point of view.

QUIZ Unit 4 • Chapter 3

A. ➤ Vocabulary: Choose the correct answer. *(24 points: 4 points each)*

1. The origin of a word can be found by looking in a(n) _____.
   a. index
   b. dictionary
   c. encyclopedia
   d. table of contents

2. You can guess the meaning of a larger word by knowing the meaning of its _____.
   a. consonants
   b. ending
   c. tense
   d. root word

3. The root word of <u>swordmaster</u>, <u>swordsman</u>, and <u>swordsmanship</u> is _____.
   a. sword
   b. man
   c. word
   d. ship

4. Word parts added to the beginning of words are called _____.
   a. root words
   b. prefixes
   c. meanings
   d. origins

5. What does the prefix *extra-* mean in the word <u>extraordinary</u>?
   a. not
   b. a lot
   c. beyond
   d. less

6. What is the root word of <u>impatience</u>?
   a. im
   b. impat
   c. patience
   d. tience

B. ➤ Text Structure/Elements of Literature: Read and choose the correct answer *(24 points: 4 points each)*

"The Basket Maker"

1   Long ago, young Miriam went to the village basket maker. She asked the woman to show her how to make beautiful baskets. The woman agreed. Miriam got right to work. She was disappointed to see that her basket was not finished in one day, so she left. Weeks later, Miriam visited the woman again. She saw lots of beautiful baskets. Miriam sighed, "I should have been more patient. Then I would have a beautiful basket of my own."

7. "The Basket Maker" is a _____.
   a. poem
   b. myth
   c. biography
   d. folktale

8. Which group of words shows that the story happened in the past?
   a. she left
   b. Long ago
   c. The woman agreed
   d. Weeks later

9. What lesson did Miriam learn?
   a. be patient
   b. always give up
   c. do not go on visits
   d. be happy about your decisions

10. Authors create characters through _____.
    a. the setting of a story
    b. what they say, think, and do
    c. writing beautiful poems about them
    d. listening to what readers say about them

QUIZ Unit 4 • Chapter 3 (continued)

11. What did Miriam do to let the woman know she was disappointed in the basket making?
  a. She quickly completed her basket.
  b. She asked for one of the woman's baskets.
  c. She screamed at the woman.
  d. She left before completing her basket.

12. Miriam's final words tell us that she _____.
  a. does not care to make another basket
  b. hopes the woman will feel sorry for her
  c. regrets not finishing her basket
  d. wishes the woman had finished her basket

C. ➤ Reading Strategies: Choose the correct answer. *(16 points: 4 points each)*

13. _____ is the exact words that characters say in a reading.
  a. Punctuation
  b. Plot
  c. Tale
  d. Dialogue

14. Stacy smiled and said, "Good morning, class." What is the dialogue in this sentence?
  a. Stacy smiled
  b. smiled and said
  c. Stacy said
  d. "Good morning, class."

15. "When will they come?" Alejandro asked his cousin. What is the dialogue in this sentence?
  a. "When will they come?"
  b. asked
  c. Alejandro asked
  d. asked his cousin

16. Janice looked at her dog and said, "I can't believe you ate my lunch!" How might Janice feel in this sentence?
  a. happy
  b. tired
  c. angry
  d. scared

D. ➤ Grammar/Usage: Choose the correct answer. *(16 points: 4 points each)*

17. _____ are often used when writers want to tell the reader when something occurred.
  a. Suffixes
  b. Adverbs
  c. Adjectives
  d. Nouns

18. On Monday, Kristina flew to Houston. The next day she flew to Dallas. What is the adverb phrase in the second sentence?
  a. she flew
  b. flew to
  c. the next day
  d. to Dallas

19. Adverbs or adverb phrases are often used near the _____ of a sentence.
  a. beginning
  b. center
  c. end
  d. action

20. Soon, I will come visit you in California. What is the adverb in this sentence?
  a. California
  b. Soon
  c. come
  d. visit

E. ➤ Writing *(20 points)*

> **Writing Prompt** Write a folktale about someone who learns a lesson. Use adverbs that show time.

QUIZ Unit 4 • Chapter 4

A. ➤ Vocabulary: Choose the correct answer. *(24 points: 4 points each)*

1. When you adjust your reading rate, you _____.
   a. read quickly by scanning the text
   b. change how fast you read
   c. read more books
   d. share the story with others

2. What is the purpose of a gloss?
   a. to make the text appear longer
   b. to help the reader find the main idea
   c. to give the reader words to use to write stories
   d. to give a short definition of an unfamiliar word

3. What should you do when reading unfamiliar words?
   a. Take time to read slowly and carefully.
   b. Have someone read the text for you.
   c. Only read text that has definitions.
   d. Write down what you read.

4. The roots of many English words come from _____.
   a. a chart containing English words
   b. school books and dictionaries
   c. other languages and cultures
   d. the back of a map

5. What is the meaning of *astro* in the word astronaut?
   a. animal
   b. star
   c. person
   d. sailor

6. The origin of a word is _____.
   a. what language it comes from
   b. the simple form
   c. its pronunciation
   d. the English form

B. ➤ Text Structure/Elements of Literature: Read and choose the correct answer. *(24 points: 4 points each)*

"Thomas Jefferson"

1   Thomas Jefferson was born on April 13, 1743, in Virginia. In 1772, he married Martha Wayles Skelton. Jefferson became active in politics at a young age. This is no surprise. As a young boy, he enjoyed learning about the law.

2   In 1776, Jefferson helped to write the Declaration of Independence. This freed the American Colonies from Great Britain. In 1801, Jefferson became president of the United States. Jefferson is an important figure in American history.

---

7. "Thomas Jefferson" is an example of a _____.
   a. narrative
   b. biography
   c. myth
   d. folktale

8. _____ texts begin with specific facts that lead to a general conclusion.
   a. Inductive
   b. Formal
   c. Deductive
   d. General

9. Which of these facts is given about Thomas Jefferson in the reading?
   a. He was fascinated by past presidents.
   b. He loved to write long letters.
   c. He helped to write the Declaration of Independence.
   d. He liked to argue with Great Britain.

QUIZ Unit 4 • Chapter 4 (continued)

10. What conclusion is drawn in the reading?
   a. Jefferson wrote many papers.
   b. Jefferson wished to lead all battles.
   c. Jefferson wanted to control Great Britain.
   d. Jefferson is an important figure in American history.

11. How do inductive texts begin?
   a. with childhood stories
   b. with organization
   c. with unrelated events
   d. with specific facts

12. _____ is when the author describes earlier events in a character's life.
   a. Predicting   **c.** Rhyme
   b. A flashback   **d.** Style

13. Which of these events happened first in the reading?
   a. Jefferson became president.
   b. Jefferson freed the colonies.
   c. Jefferson married Martha Wayles Skelton.
   d. Jefferson helped to write the Declaration of Independence.

14. Which sentence is an example of flashback from the text?
   a. In 1801, Thomas Jefferson became president of the United States.
   b. As a young boy, he enjoyed learning about the law.
   c. This freed the American Colonies.
   d. This is no surprise.

C. ➤ Reading Strategies: Choose the correct answer. *(12 points: 4 points each)*

15. To find the main idea of a paragraph, _____.
   a. take a sentence out of the paragraph and see if it sounds complete
   b. read the last sentence first
   c. read every other sentence
   d. have someone else read the paragraph

16. Supporting details _____.
   a. tell what the character will do next
   b. make the story appear to be funny
   c. give information about the main idea
   d. are questions about the story

17. Many states are home to wildlife. Which sentence is a supporting detail of this sentence?
   a. Many states are home to wildlife.
   b. New Jersey is my favorite state to visit.
   c. What is the biggest land animal?
   d. New Mexico has lots of wildlife.

D. ➤ Grammar/Usage: Choose the correct answer. *(16 points: 4 points each)*

18. A _____ must be used after a dependent clause at the beginning of a sentence.
   a. quotation
   b. comma
   c. question mark
   d. period

19. Which sentence shows an example of a dependent clause?
   a. The room looked messy. They should clean it.
   b. The children were not happy with their new toys.
   c. At the store, they bought apples.
   d. Although she had no time, she helped out anyway.

20. Which of the following is always true about a dependent clause?
   a. It is not a complete sentence.
   b. It is two sentences.
   c. It shows who is talking.
   d. It tells what happens next.

E. ➤ Writing *(20 points)*

Writing Prompt Write a short biography about someone that you think is interesting. Use inductive organization.

TEST • Unit 4

A. ➤ Reading

Saturn

My Notes

1   The first time I viewed Saturn through a telescope, my mouth dropped. "Amazing," was all I could say. This experience took place several years ago. However, each time I view Saturn, I still say, "Amazing."

2   Saturn is one of the most well-known of our planets. It is the sixth planet from the sun. It is located between the planets Jupiter and Uranus. Saturn is clearly visible from Earth. Many who have seen it describe it as a bright star.

3   The popularity of Saturn is largely due to the rings that surround it. Saturn's rings are made of rocks and ice. The layers of Saturn's rings are about 3,000 feet thick. Some scientists believe the rings surrounding Saturn formed when a small moon or comet traveled too close to the planet. The shattered object was pulled into Saturn's atmosphere. Many scientists believe there are new rings developing around Saturn.

4   The atmosphere on Saturn is very harsh. Humans would have a hard time breathing on Saturn. There are many clouds covering Saturn. There are also very strong winds on Saturn. Saturn has two main types of gas. One type is called hydrogen. The other type is called helium. Helium is the same gas that is used in special occasion balloons that float in the air. If you were able to stand on Saturn, you would find that its land is not solid like Earth's. Saturn's land is made up of a sea of liquid hydrogen that is thousands of miles deep.

5   Saturn is the second largest planet, second only to Jupiter. Saturn has 22 known moons. The moons of Saturn are similar to Earth's moon. From Saturn's moons, you can view the sun. Although it is large, it takes Saturn under 11 hours to make one full rotation, or circle. To compare, it takes Earth 24 hours to make one full rotation. This is the length of one day on Earth!

6   Although scientists know a lot about Saturn, spacecrafts are constantly exploring this mysterious planet for new findings. And I am sure my response will be the same with each new finding. Amazing.

TEST • Unit 4 (continued)

B. ➤ Reading Comprehension: Choose the correct answer. *(20 points: 2 points each)*

1. "Saturn" is a(n) _____.
   a. how-to article
   b. informational text
   c. biography
   d. myth

2. Saturn is the _____ planet from the sun.
   a. second
   b. fourth
   c. fifth
   d. sixth

3. Which planet is bigger than Saturn?
   a. Jupiter
   b. Earth
   c. Mars
   d. the sun

4. Why is Saturn considered a special planet?
   a. It is the oldest of the planets.
   b. It is the only planet that humans can visit.
   c. It has rings made of ice and rock that surround it.
   d. It has one moon that looks like 22 moons.

5. The moons of Saturn are similar to _____.
   a. Jupiter's moons
   b. Earth's moon
   c. a hydrogen sea
   d. a helium balloon

6. Why do scientists continue to explore Saturn?
   a. They hope to find new things.
   b. They want to live there soon.
   c. They hope to recreate Saturn one day.
   d. They like to amaze their friends with facts about Saturn.

7. How will humans feel if they visit Saturn?
   a. They will have a difficult time breathing.
   b. They will feel light and free to do many things.
   c. They will prefer to live there instead of on Earth.
   d. They will find it easier to breathe there than on Earth.

8. The layers of rings that surround Saturn are about _____.
   a. 3000 feet thick
   b. 2 miles long
   c. 3 inches wide
   d. 11 feet thick

9. What is one thing you can see from Saturn's moons?
   a. Earth
   b. Mars
   c. scientists
   d. the sun

10. Saturn is located between which two planets?
    a. Mercury and Earth
    b. Jupiter and Uranus
    c. Earth and Pluto
    d. Earth and the sun

TEST • Unit 4 (continued)

C. ➤ **Reading Strategies:** Choose the correct answer. *(10 points: 2 points each)*

Saturn   Earth

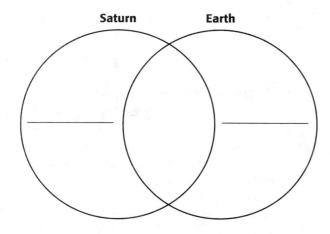

11. Use the Venn diagram to contrast. How are Saturn and Earth different?
   a. They are both planets.
   b. They both can rotate.
   c. Saturn has many moons, but Earth has no moons.
   d. It takes Saturn 11 hours to rotate, but it takes Earth 24 hours.

12. In the text, Saturn's land is compared to a _____.
   a. sea
   b. new moon
   c. bigger planet
   d. clump of material

13. Which sentence tells how the writer feels about Saturn?
   a. Saturn is one of the most well-known planets.
   b. The other type is called helium.
   c. "Amazing," was all I could say at my first Saturn sighting.
   d. Many who have seen it describe is as a bright star.

14. What is the main idea of paragraph 4?
   a. Saturn's atmosphere is harsh.
   b. Saturn is a very large planet.
   c. Scientists know a lot about Saturn.
   d. Saturn is the best planet there is.

15. Which of the following is a supporting detail in paragraph 4?
   a. This is the length of one day on Earth!
   b. There are also very strong winds on Saturn.
   c. And I am sure my response will be the same with each new finding.
   d. Saturn has 22 known moons.

D. ➤ **Elements of Literature:** Choose the correct answer. *(10 points: 2 points each)*

16. In the last line of "Saturn," the writer includes a one-word sentence to show that _____.
   a. she still finds Saturn to be a great wonder
   b. she is not sure how to end the text
   c. readers can draw their own conclusions about the text
   d. readers can predict what will happen next in the text

17. "Saturn" is written from _____ point of view.
   a. third-person
   b. first-person
   c. the reader's
   d. a planet's

18. The writer of "Saturn" _____.
   a. is upset with the planets
   b. knows a lot about Saturn
   c. is tired of studying Saturn
   d. wants to find a new planet

TEST • Unit 4 (continued)

19. The writer uses flashback in paragraph _____ of the text.
    a. 1
    b. 2
    c. 3
    d. 4

20. The author's style of writing can best be described as _____.
    a. very formal
    b. the same as all writers
    c. somewhat informal
    d. very funny

E. ➤ Vocabulary: Choose the correct answer. *(10 points: 2 points each)*

21. The word Saturday comes from the word Saturn. This example shows that _____.
    a. Saturn is a compound word
    b. history influences words in English
    c. all days of the week names come from Saturn
    d. many people helped to give Saturday its name

22. To get the most information from "Saturn," it is best to read _____.
    a. quickly and carelessly
    b. slowly and carefully
    c. just the title and the last paragraph
    d. the first and second paragraphs

23. Some scientists believe Saturn's rings were formed by a moon or a comet. Which word is the past tense of believe?
    a. believe
    b. belief
    c. liefed
    d. believed

24. How are Saturn, Jupiter, and Earth related?
    a. The sun is close to each of them.
    b. They are all located on Earth.
    c. They are all planets.
    d. People live on them.

25. The root word naut is of Latin origin. Which word contains the root word naut?
    a. nature
    b. native
    c. astronaut
    d. although

F. ➤ Grammar/Usage: Choose the correct answer. *(10 points: 2 points each)*

26. The horse was running really fast. Suddenly it stopped. What adverb tells how the horse stopped?
    a. was
    b. running
    c. really
    d. Suddenly

27. James gave Linda a sandwich, which she ate immediately. What is the relative clause in the sentence?
    a. James gave Linda
    b. Linda a sandwich
    c. which she ate immediately
    d. ate immediately

28. When Papa returns, we will make tortillas. What is the dependent clause in the sentence?
    a. When Papa returns
    b. we will
    c. will make
    d. make tortillas

29. The runner was impossible to catch. What is the infinitive in the sentence?
    a. the runner
    b. was impossible
    c. to catch
    d. the runner catch

30. Soon, the band will begin playing songs. What adverb tells when the band will begin playing?
    a. songs
    b. begin
    c. will
    d. soon

VISIONS B Assessment Program • Copyright © Heinle

TEST • Unit 4 (continued)

G. ➤ **Writing Conventions:** Choose the correct answer. *(10 points: 2 points each)*

31. The floor is _____ when wet.
   a. slipry
   b. slippery
   c. sleepy
   d. sleepery

32. Which number is written correctly?
   a. 150,0
   b. 8770,
   c. 12,357
   d. 3,942107

33. We both _____ that our mother was right.
   a. new
   b. noew
   c. kneow
   d. knew

34. "please wait here," said the crossing guard. Which word needs a capital letter in the sentence?
   a. please
   b. said
   c. crossing
   d. guard

35. Consuela is a Mexican american, just like her neighbor. Which word needs a capital letter in the sentence?
   a. is
   b. american
   c. her
   d. neighbor

H. ➤ **Editing:** Read and choose the correct answer. *(10 points: 2 points each)*

1 When I awake in the morning, the <u>son</u> is always shining <u>threw</u> my window.
2 Sometimes is shines very brightly and lights up my entire bedroom.
3 I like to picture that I live on the surface of the sun where it ever gets dark or cold.
4 I would look out of my window every morning and admire the beauty of the planets moons, and stars as they travel through space.

36. In sentence 1, <u>son</u> is best written _____.
   a. sun
   b. san
   c. sone
   d. as it is written

37. In sentence 1, <u>threw</u> is best written _____.
   a. throo
   b. theroow
   c. through
   d. as it is written

38. What change should you make to sentence 2?
   a. change *is* to *it*
   b. change *brightly* to *bright*
   c. change *up* to *out*
   d. make no change

39. What change should you make to sentence 3?
   a. change *picture* to *pikture*
   b. change *sun* to *son*
   c. change *ever* to *never*
   d. make no change

TEST • Unit 4 (continued)

40. What change should you make to
sentence 4?
   a. change *look* to *looking*
   b. change *and* to *but*
   c. add a comma after *planets*
   d. add a comma after *travel*

I. ➤ Writing (20 points)

> **Writing Prompt** Write a fictional story
> about a trip to space. Use first-person
> point of view to tell your story. Use the
> Planning Guide to help you write.

Planning Guide
❏ Ask yourself the following questions:
   a. How will I get to space?
   b. Where will I go once I am there?
   c. What will I do?
   d. What will I see?
❏ Use the pronouns I, me, and my in your
  story.
❏ Be sure that your story has a beginning,
  middle, and end.

VISIONS B Assessment Program • Copyright © Heinle

Name _____ Date _____

Grade ☐

QUIZ Unit 5 • Chapter 1

A. ➤ Vocabulary: Read and choose the correct answer. *(24 points: 4 points each)*

1. "Adios," said the woman as she exited the room. The Spanish word adios means _____.
   a. hello
   b. good-bye
   c. thank you
   d. mister

2. Carlos blubbers when his brother does not share his games. Another word for blubbers is _____.
   a. plays
   b. eats
   c. cries
   d. laughs

3. A(n) _____ is a group of letters added to the beginning of a word.
   a. suffix
   b. prefix
   c. plural
   d. adjective

4. Selena _____ her suitcase after her trip.
   a. unpacked
   b. made
   c. packing
   d. pack

5. A person who is not polite is _____.
   a. happy
   b. impolite
   c. polite
   d. sad

6. The science test was impossible. Which word in the sentence has a prefix?
   a. science
   b. test
   c. was
   d. impossible

B. ➤ Text Structure/Elements of Literature: Read and choose the correct answer. *(28 points: 4 points each)*

"Marisol's Monday Meeting"

1   "Hello, Marisol," said Ms. Hilda. "You have been doing a great job on all of your class assignments."

2   Marisol smiled at the principal and said, "Yes, I have been working very hard on everything."

3   Ms. Hilda smiled back and said, "We are happy that you are adjusting to your new school. We are very proud of you!"

---

7. "Marisol's Monday Meeting" is an example of a _____ story.
   a. nonfiction
   b. science fiction
   c. narrative
   d. informational

8. Who is speaking in the text?
   a. only Ms. Hilda
   b. only Marisol
   c. Ms. Hilda and Marisol
   d. Ms. Hilda and another student

9. What happens at the end of the story?
   a. Marisol leaves Ms. Hilda's office upset.
   b. Ms. Hilda says that Marisol is doing a good job.
   c. Ms. Hilda punishes Marisol.
   d. Marisol gives Ms. Hilda an award.

10. A narrative story must have _____.
    a. a title and a happy ending
    b. at least three characters
    c. animals who talk
    d. a beginning, a middle, and an end

QUIZ Unit 5 • Chapter 1 (continued)

11. Dialogue in a narrative shows how characters _____.
    a. play games together
    b. speak to one another
    c. become friends
    d. help each other

12. Every story has a _____.
    a. scary ending
    b. point of view
    c. third person
    d. rhyme

13. A story told using the words I, me, us, and we is written in the _____.
    a. first person
    b. second person
    c. third person
    d. fourth person

C. ➤ **Reading Strategies:** Choose the correct answer. (16 points: 4 points each)

14. Guessing what will happen next in a story is called _____.
    a. reading
    b. predicting
    c. summarizing
    d. plotting

15. When you predict, you make a _____ about the future.
    a. guess
    b. mark
    c. meaning
    d. story

16. Emanuel is hungry. He is on his way to the kitchen. You can predict that he will _____.
    a. sleep
    b. run
    c. clean
    d. eat

17. Lorena is upset that her grandparents are moving. You can predict that she will begin to _____.
    a. laugh
    b. giggle
    c. cry
    d. jump

D. ➤ **Grammar/Usage:** Choose the correct answer. (12 points: 4 points each)

18. The present perfect tense of a verb shows an action that happened in the past but has an effect on the _____.
    a. past
    b. present
    c. noun
    d. verb

19. Which sentence is an example of the present perfect tense?
    a. Arnold wants a ball.
    b. Pete looks at the sky.
    c. Anel has studied hard.
    d. Tim runs fast.

20. Which sentence is an example of present perfect tense?
    a. Ana looked sadly at the plate.
    b. Maria has eaten three bananas.
    c. Alex plays the flute.
    d. Blanca calls her sister.

E. ➤ **Writing** (20 points)

Writing Prompt Write a narrative about how one person helps another person who does not speak English. Use dialogue in your narrative.

VISIONS B Assessment Program • Copyright © Heinle

QUIZ Unit 5 • Chapter 2

A. ➤ Vocabulary: Choose the correct answer. *(24 points: 4 points each)*

1. Synonyms are _____.
   a. compound words
   b. adjectives in sentences
   c. words that mean almost the same thing
   d. words that look and sound the same

2. Arturo <u>yanks</u> the rug from underneath the couch. A synonym for <u>yanks</u> is _____.
   a. pushes
   b. pulls
   c. feels
   d. runs

3. Alfredo <u>skims</u> the first page of the book by moving his eyes quickly down the page. A synonym for <u>skims</u> is _____.
   a. quietly breaks into two parts
   b. quickly looks over
   c. touches
   d. writes

4. An adverb is a word that _____.
   a. tells who does what
   b. tells what happens next
   c. describes a verb, adjective or other adverb
   d. describes a person, place, or thing

5. His elbow was painfully sore. What is the adverb in the sentence?
   a. His
   b. elbow
   c. painfully
   d. sore

6. Karina slowly picks up her favorite book. What is the adverb in the sentence?
   a. Karina
   b. slowly
   c. picks
   d. her

B. ➤ Text Structure/Elements of Literature: Read and choose the correct answer. *(28 points: 4 points each)*

> **"Nathan's Joy"**
>
> 1   Nathan Bergis was born on December 2, 1934. As a young child, he became very interested in music. At age five, he began taking piano lessons. He also took voice lessons. He learned very quickly. He won his first award for playing the piano in 1943. He was only nine years old.
>
> 2   Over the years, Nathan has won over 100 awards from around the world. Nathan is much older now, but he still enjoys playing the piano and singing.

7. "Nathan's Joy" is an example of a(n) _____.
   a. fantasy
   b. autobiography
   c. drama
   d. biography

8. A biography describes _____ in a person's life.
   a. boring details
   b. happiness
   c. important events
   d. sad events

9. A reading that includes facts and information about a person is called a
   _____.
   a. play
   b. biography
   c. bibliography
   d. drama

10. A drama is a _____.
   a. play
   b. book
   c. story
   d. biography

QUIZ Unit 5 • Chapter 2 (continued)

"The Surprise"

Wanda walks through the door of her house.

Wanda: What are you doing home so early, Mom?

Wanda's mom holds up a puppy with a red bow around its neck.

Mom: I wanted to surprise you with something you have always wanted.

---

11. The first line in "The Surprise" is an example of a(n) _____.
    a. act
    b. stage direction
    c. character
    d. scene

12. "The Surprise" is a(n) _____.
    a. biography
    b. drama
    c. autobiography
    d. poem

13. _____ tell how the characters will act.
    a. Stage directions
    b. Dialogues
    c. Workers
    d. Actions

C. ➤ Reading Strategies: Choose the correct answer. *(16 points: 4 points each)*

14. To describe how things are similar is to _____.
    a. compare
    b. contrast
    c. look for clues
    d. write a sentence

15. To describe how things are different is to _____.
    a. use new vocabulary
    b. find synonyms
    c. write
    d. contrast

16. Angela ate pizza at 6:00. Sam ate tacos at 6:00. How can you compare these sentences?
    a. Angela ate pizza.
    b. Sam ate tacos.
    c. Angela and Sam ate different foods.
    d. Angela and Sam both ate at 6:00.

17. Ron rode his bike to school. Leo walked to school. How can you contrast these sentences?
    a. Ron and Leo are both boys.
    b. Ron and Leo both go to school.
    c. Ron rode his bike, but Leo walked.
    d. Ron is tall, but Leo is short.

D. ➤ Grammar/Usage: Choose the correct answer. *(12 points: 4 points each)*

18. The _____ describes an action in progress in the past.
    a. present perfect tense
    b. past tense
    c. past continuous tense
    d. future tense

19. Which action is past continuous?
    a. The bird was flying.
    b. The chipmunk is eating.
    c. Kelly is walking.
    d. I am going.

20. Which action is past continuous?
    a. My brother is watching TV.
    b. We were watching the game.
    c. We will eat soon.
    d. The flowers were nice.

E. ➤ Writing *(20 points)*

Writing Prompt Write a scene for a play. Tell how someone dealt with a problem. Use past continuous verbs.

VISIONS B Assessment Program • Copyright © Heinle

Name _____ Date _____

Grade

QUIZ Unit 5 • Chapter 3

A. ➤ Vocabulary: Choose the correct answer. *(24 points: 4 points each)*

1. Where might you find the definition of a science word that you do not know?
   a. on a timeline
   b. on a map
   c. in the glosses
   d. in a notebook

2. In science textbooks, important words are often _____.
   a. left out
   b. in bold print
   c. given as pictures
   d. not used

3. In science textbooks, important terms are used as _____.
   a. pictures
   b. the title of the book
   c. headings
   d. writing questions

4. You may use a dictionary to _____.
   a. learn new words
   b. practice reading
   c. find subjects to write about
   d. locate a library

5. The prefix *tele-* means _____.
   a. near
   b. far
   c. close
   d. behind

6. Which of the following words has the prefix *tele-*?
   a. towel
   b. telescope
   c. table
   d. tell

B. ➤ Text Structure/Elements of Literature: Read and choose the correct answer. *(28 points: 4 points each)*

"Elephants"

Amazing Animals

1   Elephants are amazing. They are the largest animals that live on land. They can live to be 60 years old. Elephants are very strong. They can be trained to carry heavy supplies and people. Long ago, there were many types of elephants that roamed the land. Today, only two types of elephants can be found. These are the African elephant and the Asian elephant.

---

7. This reading is most likely part of a _____.
   a. song
   b. poem
   c. textbook
   d. dictionary

8. A book written specifically to teach students is called a(n) _____.
   a. chart
   b. poem
   c. textbook
   d. encyclopedia

9. _____ for this reading would show pictures of elephants.
   a. Subheadings
   b. Graphics
   c. Headings
   d. Details and examples

10. _____ divide major sections of textbooks into smaller sections.
    a. Subheadings
    b. Pictures
    c. Writings
    d. Examples

QUIZ Unit 5 • Chapter 3 (continued)

11. What is the subheading of "Elephants"?
    a. African Elephants
    b. Largest Animal
    c. Amazing Animals
    d. Land Elephants

12. Titles of major sections are called _____.
    a. headings
    b. subheadings
    c. glosses
    d. chapters

13. _____ language helps you to picture actions and is very precise.
    a. English
    b. Adjective
    c. Descriptive
    d. Noun

C. ➤ Reading Strategies: Choose the correct answer. (16 points: 4 points each)

14. One way to learn as you read a textbook is to write _____.
    a. a poem
    b. an outline
    c. definitions
    d. answers

15. An outline should include _____.
    a. the author's personal thoughts
    b. pictures to help you remember
    c. comparisons to other texts
    d. a list of major points from the reading

16. You read a text about teeth. One major part is about teeth cleaning. Where should teeth cleaning be placed in an outline?
    a. by a Roman numeral
    b. by a letter
    c. near a symbol
    d. on the back of the page

17. You read a text about sports. One detail talks about wearing a safety helmet. Under which major heading should you write information about wearing a safety helmet?
    a. Sports Heroes
    b. Basketball
    c. Safety in Sports
    d. Favorite Teams

D. ➤ Grammar/Usage: Choose the correct answer. (12 points: 4 points each)

18. A verb in the present tense must _____ its subject.
    a. change
    b. agree with
    c. compare
    d. contrast

19. Andrea _____ three miles a day. Which verb agrees with the subject in the present tense?
    a. running
    b. runs
    c. ran
    d. runner

20. Sanyo and Liza _____ in a choir. Which verb agrees with the subject in the present tense?
    a. sang
    b. singer
    c. sing
    d. sung

E. ➤ Writing (20 points)

Writing Prompt Write an informational text about something you know a lot about. Explain your topic clearly.

VISIONS B Assessment Program • Copyright © Heinle

Name _____ Date _____

QUIZ Unit 5 • Chapter 4

A. ➤ Vocabulary: Choose the correct answer. *(24 points: 4 points each)*

1. You can use _____ to learn words about art.
   a. context clues
   b. puzzles
   c. games
   d. photographs

2. A _____ is a person or animal in a story.
   a. setting
   b. plot
   c. character
   d. conclusion

3. A _____ is an idea for a story.
   a. narrative
   b. definition
   c. concept
   d. costume

4. Which suffix might help tell where a person is from?
   a. *-ing*
   b. *-ed*
   c. *-s*
   d. *-ian*

5. A person who is from the state of Texas would most likely be called a _____.
   a. Texaser
   b. Tex
   c. Texas
   d. Texan

6. A person who works at a library is a _____.
   a. library
   b. book
   c. librarian
   d. builder

B. ➤ Text Structure/Elements of Literature: Read and choose the correct answer. *(28 points: 4 points each)*

> "Peanut Butter and Banana Sandwich"
>
> 1   First you will need to get your ingredients. You will need one tablespoon of peanut butter, half of a banana, and two pieces of bread. You will also need a round-edged knife or spreader.
>
> 2   First, slice the banana into six pieces. Place the bananas on one piece of bread. Next, take the other piece of bread. Spread the peanut butter all over the bread. Finally, put the two pieces of bread together. Enjoy!

7. This reading is a _____.
   a. mystery
   b. how-to text
   c. poem
   d. scene from a play

8. _____ are drawings or other artwork that help you understand a text.
   a. Comics
   b. Illustrations
   c. Words
   d. Sentences

9. Which of these illustrations would best help you to understand "Peanut Butter and Banana Sandwich"?
   a. a drawing of the author of the reading
   b. a drawing of the peanut butter and bananas
   c. a drawing of someone eating the sandwich
   d. a drawing of someone making the sandwich

QUIZ Unit 5 • Chapter 4 (continued)

10. A how-to book should include _____.
    a. dialogue
    b. a step-by-step explanation
    c. a problem
    d. characters

11. Style is the way writers use _____ to express themselves.
    a. people
    b. language
    c. poems
    d. plays

12. A writer who uses informal language in his writing _____.
    a. does not write a lot about the topic
    b. may not use complete sentences
    c. only uses one character in a reading
    d. forgets to write an end

13. Enjoy! This phrase from the text is an example of _____.
    a. a friendly letter
    b. informal writing
    c. conversation
    d. a metaphor

C. ➤ Reading Strategies: Choose the correct answer. (16 points: 4 points each)

14. _____ helps you make inferences about what you read.
    a. A textbook
    b. Text evidence
    c. A telescope
    d. A television

15. Pedro smiled and jumped up and down when he won second prize. Based on the text evidence, you know that Pedro is _____.
    a. shy about winning
    b. angry that he did not win first place
    c. bored and wants to go home
    d. happy that he won second place

16. What text evidence would make you infer that a reading is fantasy?
    a. The birds fly.
    b. The children can fly.
    c. The animals play.
    d. The plants grow.

17. What text evidence supports the inference that it rained?
    a. The wind blew hard.
    b. The sun shined brightly.
    c. There were puddles on the ground.
    d. The clouds were black.

D. ➤ Grammar/Usage: Choose the correct answer. (12 points: 4 points each)

18. If you clean your room, you can go outside. This is a _____ sentence.
    a. past tense
    b. present conditional
    c. perfect tense
    d. past perfect tense

19. A present conditional sentence has _____.
    a. a dependent and an independent clause
    b. only a dependent clause
    c. only an independent clause
    d. only one clause

20. A conditional sentence usually begins with the word _____.
    a. if
    b. as
    c. like
    d. but

E. ➤ Writing (20 points)

Writing Prompt Write a paragraph describing how to do something. Use step-by-step details. Include illustrations and captions.

VISIONS B Assessment Program • Copyright © Heinle

Name _____ Date _____

Grade

TEST • Unit 5

A. ➤ Reading

How to Use the Library

My Notes

1   To begin using the library, you must first apply for a library card. A library card will allow you to borrow books. It will also allow the library to keep a record of the books that you have borrowed.

2   To begin your library journey, first look for a librarian at the circulation desk. Next, tell the librarian that you would like to apply for a library card. The librarian will give you a library card application. The library card application has a place for you to write your name, address, and telephone number. The librarian will process your completed application. You are now ready to begin exploring the different areas of the library.

3   You can find many types of books, such as fiction, non-fiction, and science-fiction books, at the library. All books are arranged in alphabetical order by the author's last name. Most books are available for you to check out. There are also books available in the reference section of the library. Many people use these books to help them research information and facts on a topic. Reference books include dictionaries, encyclopedias, textbooks, magazines, and newspapers. Reference books may only be used at the library.

4   Libraries have special areas for public use. Many libraries have computers and videos for people to use. Libraries try to arrange their hours so that you may spend as much time as you wish there. There are, however, a few simple rules you must follow. You must talk quietly at all times. You may never run. You must always respect others and the items in the library.

5   When you have found the books that you want, go to the "check out" desk. The librarian will stamp the inside of each book with the date the book must be returned. Make sure to return the book or you will pay a small fine for each day that it is late. Enjoy reading your books!

TEST • Unit 5 (continued)

B. ➤ Reading Comprehension: Choose the correct answer. *(10 points: 2 points each)*

1. "How to Use the Library" is an example of a _____.
   a. how-to article
   b. first-person narrative
   c. play
   d. letter

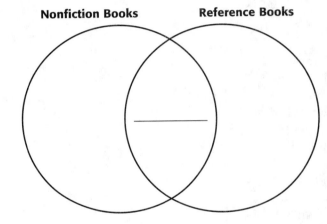

Nonfiction Books   **Reference Books**

2. Use the Venn Diagram to compare and contrast. How are nonfiction books and reference books similar?
   a. both include facts
   b. both have happy endings
   c. both are colorful
   d. both can be read quickly

3. The picture of the books in the text shows _____.
   a. the total number of books available at a library
   b. examples of books you can find at the library
   c. which books you read last year
   d. books that the librarian likes

4. According to the reading, libraries are _____.
   a. hard to use
   b. easy to use
   c. funny
   d. made of wood

5. Ana will go to the library on Saturday for the first time. Predict what she will do first.
   a. check out a book
   b. search the shelves
   c. run in circles
   d. apply for a library card

6. Most people go to the library to _____.
   a. find information
   b. learn how to read
   c. meet new friends
   d. play computer games

7. If you need to research a topic on a country, you may choose to look in the _____ section.
   a. children's
   b. fiction
   c. computer
   d. reference

8. One rule to follow while visiting the library is _____.
   a. spend a lot of time there
   b. speak a lot to the librarian
   c. talk quietly at all times
   d. keep a record of the books you read

9. Based on the text, you can best conclude that libraries are good places to find _____.
   a. lots of plays
   b. math problems
   c. information
   d. artwork

10. Most libraries stamp your book to show you the date the book is due. Another word for stamp is _____.
    a. kick
    b. mark
    c. take
    d. read

VISIONS B Assessment Program • Copyright © Heinle

TEST • Unit 5 *(continued)*

C. ➤ Reading Strategies: Choose the correct answer. *(10 points: 2 points each)*

11. You can predict that a person reading this text will _____.
    a. stop reading books
    b. want to use the library soon
    c. go to a bookstore
    d. try to make his own library

12. How is a library different from a bookstore?
    a. A library is for borrowing books. A bookstore is for buying books.
    b. A library is for sharing books. A bookstore is to search for new books.
    c. A library is big. A bookstore is small.
    d. A library is round. A bookstore is square.

13. What topic should you include in an outline based on "How to Use the Library"?
    a. Your Neighborhood Librarian
    b. Getting a Library Card
    c. Showing Your Friends the Library
    d. Buying Books from the Librarian

14. Text evidence is _____.
    a. informational books
    b. reference sources
    c. words that tell who characters are
    d. words in the text that give information

15. Based on text evidence, you can conclude that the writer of "How to Use the Library" _____.
    a. does not own any books
    b. stays away from libraries
    c. has visited a library before
    d. is new to the town

D. ➤ Elements of Literature: Choose the correct answer. *(10 points: 2 points each)*

16. What is descriptive language?
    a. precise information that gives details on a topic
    b. vocabulary that tells what the writer is thinking
    c. verbs that show action
    d. nouns that act like adjectives

17. In "How to Use the Library," the writer uses descriptive language to describe _____.
    a. the librarian
    b. buildings around the library
    c. the library card application
    d. people who come to the library

18. The writer of "How to Use the Library" presents information by _____.
    a. writing rhyming words in each sentence
    b. using dialogue to show what the librarian is thinking
    c. giving the main idea and supporting details
    d. writing a resolution

19. _____ tells the story using words <u>he</u>, <u>she</u> and <u>they</u>.
    a. Third-person point of view
    b. First-person point of view
    c. A place
    d. An object

20. "How to Use the Library" is told from the _____ point of view.
    a. writer's
    b. librarian's
    c. user's
    d. book's

TEST • Unit 5 (continued)

E. ➤ Vocabulary: Choose the correct answer. *(10 points: 2 points each)*

21. The library card has a place for you to write your name, address, and telephone number. What is the prefix in the word telephone?
    a. telephone
    b. one
    c. phone
    d. tele

22. You must talk quietly at all times in the library. Which word is the adverb in the sentence?
    a. talk
    b. quietly
    c. times
    d. library

23. You must not run in the library. A synonym for run is _____.
    a. jog
    b. skip
    c. crawl
    d. move

24. What is the suffix in the word librarian?
    a. ian
    b. ing
    c. lib
    d. rar

25. Where in the library can you find definitions for words you don't know?
    a. children's
    b. fiction
    c. reference
    d. video

F. ➤ Grammar/Usage: Choose the correct answer. *(10 points: 2 points each)*

26. Maria has checked out a book. This sentence is an example of _____.
    a. past tense
    b. simple tense
    c. present perfect tense
    d. future tense

27. The child was walking in the park. This sentence is an example of _____.
    a. past tense
    b. past continuous tense
    c. verb
    d. noun

28. If you return the library book late, you will pay a small fee. This sentence is an example of a _____.
    a. present conditional
    b. past verbs
    c. future events
    d. adverb phrases

29. Which is an example of a present conditional?
    a. If you check out a book, you should return it on time.
    b. Mr. Lopez knows a lot about computers and how to fix them.
    c. We meet at the library every week to study.
    d. That book has a lot of information for my report.

30. The students read books. The subject and verb in this sentence _____.
    a. look the same
    b. agree
    c. happen in the future
    d. do not agree

TEST • Unit 5 *(continued)*

G. ➤ **Writing Conventions:** Choose the correct answer. *(10 points: 2 points each)*

31. Andrea and Ana went to _____ house. Which word correctly completes the sentence?
    a. they're
    b. their
    c. they are
    d. there

32. Maria said *adios* to her family. <u>Adios</u> is written in italics to show it is _____.
    a. a nice word
    b. an action word
    c. in another language
    d. an adjective

33. Titles and headings should start with _____.
    a. capital letters
    b. smaller letters than the text
    c. part of the story
    d. italic type

34. William is _____ breakfast. Which spelling correctly completes the sentence?
    a. makeing
    b. maykeing
    c. making
    d. mackeeng

35. Scene 2: (Robert picks up the cup and drinks from it.) These stage directions should be written in _____.
    a. all capital letters
    b. all small letters
    c. italics
    d. darker print

H. ➤ **Editing:** Read and choose the correct answer. *(10 points: 2 points each)*

1 Yesterday, Alex <u>goed</u> to the store for his mother to buy a loaf of bread.
2 He di'dnt see the kind of bread his mother wanted.
3 He asked the man who worked there for help.
4 The man showed Alex when to find the bread that he wanted.
5 Alex thanked the man after leaving the store.

36. In sentence 1, <u>goed</u> should be written _____.
    a. left   c. go
    b. went   d. gone

37. What change should you make to sentence 2?
    a. change *di'dnt* to *didn't*
    b. change *see* to *saw*
    c. change *waned* to *wanting*
    d. make no change

38. What change should you make to sentence 3?
    a. change *asked* to *ask*
    b. change *worked* to *working*
    c. change the period after *help* to a question mark
    d. make no change

39. What change should you make to sentence 4?
    a. change *showed* to *show*
    b. change *when* to *where*
    c. change *that* to *who*
    d. make no change

40. What change should you make to sentence 5?
    a. change *thanked* to *thanks*
    b. add a comma after *thanked*
    c. change *after* to *before*
    d. make no change

TEST • Unit 5 *(continued)*

I. ➤ Writing *(20 points)*

Writing Prompt Write a how-to text explaining how to do something that you know a lot about. Be sure to include steps in the process. Use clear directions. Use the Planning Guide to help you write.

Planning Guide
❏ Ask yourself the following questions:
  a. What do I know how to do?
  b. What are the steps involved in the process?
❏ Use the answers to your questions to write your how-to text.
❏ Read your text to make sure that your information is clearly written.

VISIONS B Assessment Program • Copyright © Heinle

QUIZ Unit 6 • Chapter 1

A. ➤ Vocabulary: Choose the correct answer. *(24 points: 4 points each)*

1. Which word belongs on a word wheel for <u>expedition</u>?
   a. pathetic
   b. rooster
   c. exposition
   d. journey

2. Which word belongs on a word wheel for <u>climate</u>?
   a. climb
   b. path
   c. plant
   d. tropical

3. Jake loves astronomy and is <u>fascinated</u> by the solar system. A synonym for <u>fascinated</u> is _____.
   a. very bored
   b. very interested
   c. worried
   d. lucky

4. I enjoy hiking because of the <u>fabulous</u> views. A synonym for <u>fabulous</u> is _____.
   a. wonderful
   b. horrible
   c. fair
   d. average

5. We followed the <u>route</u> along the river. A <u>route</u> is a _____.
   a. path along which one travels
   b. box of supplies one brings on a trip
   c. job on an expedition
   d. boat to travel

6. A(n) _____ lists synonyms for words.
   a. thesaurus
   b. dictionary
   c. encyclopedia
   d. atlas

B. ➤ Text Structure/Elements of Literature: Read and choose the correct answer. *(16 points: 4 points each)*

"Amelia Earhart"

1   Amelia Earhart was born on July 24, 1897. She served as a nurse in World War I and took her first airplane ride in 1920. Within a few days, she took her first flying lesson. She bought her own plane six months later. She was not a gifted pilot, but she practiced all of the time. She became the first woman to fly across the Atlantic Ocean on June 18, 1928.

---

7. "Amelia Earhart" is a(n) _____.
   a. realistic adventure fiction
   b. personal narrative
   c. informational text
   d. fiction

8. Which word best describes Amelia?
   a. brave
   b. weak
   c. lazy
   d. angry

9. Informational texts contain _____.
   a. fictional characters
   b. events that really happened
   c. fictional stories
   d. fables

10. What kind of person do you think Amelia Earhart was?
    a. adventurous
    b. bored
    c. lonely
    d. shy

QUIZ Unit 6 • Chapter 1 *(continued)*

C. ➤ Reading Strategies: Choose the correct answer. *(16 points: 4 points each)*

11. _____ tells a story told in the order that the events actually happened.
    a. Reverse order
    b. Chronological order
    c. Mood
    d. Setting

12. Jake went to the store. Then he went home. What did Jake do first?
    a. went home
    b. went to the store
    c. went to the park
    d. none of the above

13. Carolyn went to her friend's house after work. Before work, she cleaned the house. What did Carolyn do first?
    a. went to her friend's house
    b. went to work
    c. cleaned the house
    d. none of the above

14. Wayne laced up his skates. Then he stopped at Fred's house. They went skating together. What did Wayne do last?
    a. went skating
    b. laced up his skates
    c. stopped at Fred's house
    d. bought new skates

D. ➤ Grammar/Usage: Choose the correct answer. *(24 points: 4 points each)*

15. An appositive is a word or phrase that follows a(n) _____ in order to give extra information about it.
    a. regular verb
    b. irregular verb
    c. noun
    d. adjective

16. Use a _____ before and after an appositive if it is in the middle of a sentence.
    a. comma
    b. semicolon
    c. colon
    d. period

17. If an appositive comes at the end of a sentence, use a _____ at the beginning of the appositive.
    a. period
    b. colon
    c. comma
    d. semicolon

18. I called you Madeline just to say hi. Commas are needed before and after _____.
    a. Madeline
    b. I
    c. you
    d. hi

19. The new kid on the team whom I met yesterday helped win the match. Commas are needed before and after _____.
    a. new kid
    b. whom I met yesterday
    c. on the team
    d. helped win the match

20. Our teacher Mrs. Smith gave a great speech. Commas are needed before and after _____.
    a. Our teacher
    b. teacher
    c. Mrs. Smith
    d. great speech

E. ➤ Writing *(20 points)*

> **Writing Prompt** Write an informational paragraph about a famous explorer. Describe the challenges the explorer faced.

QUIZ Unit 6 • Chapter 2

A. ➤ Vocabulary: Choose the correct answer. *(24 points: 4 points each)*

1. You can guess the meanings of new words by using the _____ of a sentence.
   a. dictionary
   b. context
   c. definition
   d. meaning

2. She took a <u>portion</u> of the cake. <u>Portion</u> means _____.
   a. all
   b. a piece of a larger thing
   c. an ingredient
   d. a recipe

3. A _____ is a word part added to the beginning of the word.
   a. suffix
   b. verb
   c. compound word
   d. prefix

4. We decided it was <u>impractical</u> to go to the circus. What is the <u>prefix</u> in <u>impractical</u>?
   a. practical
   b. *im-*
   c. impractical
   d. *-al*

5. He was <u>unable</u> to function. What is the prefix in <u>unable</u>?
   a. *-able*
   b. unable
   c. *-ab-*
   d. *un-*

6. <u>Intolerable</u> means _____.
   a. not tolerable
   b. not difficult
   c. kind of smooth
   d. very easy

B. ➤ Text Structure/Elements of Literature: Read and choose the correct answer. *(20 points: 4 points each)*

"Jason's Sky"

1   Jason looked at all the bright lights in the sky. He ran to the end of the street. He was sweating and his heart was racing. He wasn't sure he could go any farther, but he knew he couldn't give up. He had seen the bright lights in the sky. He knew Father's spaceship was scheduled to land any moment. He was sure the lights meant that Father was arriving home from work just on the other side of the hill.

7. "Jason's Sky" is _____.
   a. realistic adventure fiction
   b. a personal narrative
   c. science fiction
   d. a fable

8. Where does the story take place?
   a. at Jason's house
   b. on a street
   c. at an airport
   d. on a spaceship

9. The mood in "Jason's Sky" is _____.
   a. anger
   b. sadness
   c. excitement
   d. humor

10. Which sentence from the story best helps to set the mood?
   a. Jason looked at all the bright lights in the sky.
   b. He ran to the end of the street.
   c. He had seen the bright lights in the sky.
   d. He was sweating and his heart was racing.

QUIZ Unit 6 • Chapter 2 (continued)

11. "Jason's Sky" best shows the reader _____.
    a. how a play looks
    b. what might happen in the future
    c. a lesson taught in a story
    d. a true story about a real person

C. ➤ **Reading Strategies:** Choose the correct answer. *(12 points: 4 points each)*

12. _____ are what the writer wants you to "see" while reading.
    a. Physical strengths
    b. Mental images
    c. Different languages
    d. Predictions

13. Which of these sentences helps to provide the best mental image?
    a. She was shaking like a leaf.
    b. She was scared.
    c. She was nervous.
    d. She was happy.

14. Which sentence creates the best mental image?
    a. Jake ran quickly.
    b. Jake ran on his feet.
    c. Jake ran like the wind.
    d. Jake ran.

D. ➤ **Grammar/Usage:** Choose the correct answer. *(24 points: 4 points each)*

15. The past perfect tense is used to talk about actions that _____.
    a. are taking place now
    b. are going to take place
    c. have already taken place
    d. will never take place

16. She felt pressure like she _____never imagined.
    a. did
    b. had
    c. was
    d. can

17. Linda had never _____ she would be elected.
    a. believe
    b. belief
    c. believed
    d. believing

18. We _____ expected our friends to arrive soon.
    a. has
    b. had
    c. been
    d. did

19. I had _____ her at the park.
    a. see
    b. saw
    c. seen
    d. meet

20. Sam had _____ lunch before noon.
    a. eat
    b. ate
    c. aten
    d. eaten

E. ➤ **Writing** *(20 points)*

Writing Prompt Write a paragraph about an event that takes place in the future. Make up a character with a problem to face and describe how the character solves the problem.

VISIONS B Assessment Program • Copyright © Heinle

QUIZ Unit 6 • Chapter 3

A. ➤ Vocabulary: Choose the correct answer. *(24 points: 4 points each)*

1. A(n) _____ is what a word usually means.
   a. antonym
   b. connotative meaning
   c. denotative meaning
   d. synonym

2. The _____ is the images or feelings that a word can give.
   a. connotative meaning
   b. denotative meaning
   c. synonym
   d. antonym

3. Which sentence shows a connotative meaning of the word "home"?
   a. I am going <u>home</u> at noon today.
   b. I feel at <u>home</u> here: This hotel is so comfortable.
   c. Let's stay <u>home</u> today. It is too cold to go out.
   d. Go <u>home</u> now.

4. Her eyes danced as she laughed. Her eyes _____.
   a. jumped
   b. moved around
   c. shut
   d. sparkled

5. Even though the room was crowded, it was a sea of calm. The room was _____.
   a. dark
   b. loud
   c. quiet
   d. lively

6. The clouds pranced boldly across the sky. The clouds were _____.
   a. moving
   b. shrinking
   c. hiding
   d. laughing

B. ➤ Text Structure/Elements of Literature: Read and choose the correct answer. *(16 points: 4 points each)*

"Mrs. Smith"

1   Mrs. Smith stood up and began to speak. "We must not allow the community center to close. It is important that we fight to keep it up and running. I am counting on each of you to do your part. It should remain the center of our neighborhood."

7. "Mrs. Smith" is an example of a(n) _____.
   a. adventure fiction
   b. personal narrative
   c. informational text
   d. persuasive speech

8. Who is the audience in "Mrs. Smith"?
   a. Mrs. Smith
   b. her neighbors
   c. her class
   d. the principal

9. One purpose of a persuasive speech is to _____.
   a. tell a story
   b. provide a description
   c. persuade an audience
   d. reveal the characters

10. What is the message of Mrs. Smith's speech?
    a. to get a new community center in the neighborhood
    b. to show people how a community center works
    c. to tell people why they should build a community center
    d. to stop the community center from closing

QUIZ Unit 6 • Chapter 3 (continued)

C. ➤ Reading Strategies: Choose the correct *answer. (16 points: 4 points each)*

11. Ann jogged in place. Then she stretched and took her place at the starting line. What conclusion can you draw from the sentence?
   a. Ann is ready to run.
   b. Ann is going to school.
   c. Ann is going to sleep.
   d. Ann is ready to stretch.

12. Jackie worked all day and then went home to take a nap. What conclusion can you draw from the sentence?
   a. Jackie was tired.
   b. Jackie was ready to work.
   c. Jackie left work early.
   d. Jackie wanted to watch television.

13. My cat ran away this morning. I hope I find her. What conclusion can you draw from the sentence?
   a. The cat came home.
   b. The cat is still in the house.
   c. The cat left in the evening.
   d. The cat is missing.

14. Larry stayed up very late and studied for the test. What conclusion can you draw from the sentence?
   a. Larry got a good night's sleep.
   b. Larry did not get much sleep.
   c. Larry likes to read.
   d. Larry is a teacher.

D. ➤ Grammar/Usage: Choose the correct answer. *(24 points: 4 points each)*

15. _____ are parts of sentences that have a subject and a verb.
   a. Nouns
   b. Clauses
   c. Sentences
   d. Adjectives

16. A(n) _____ needs more information to make sense.
   a. independent clause
   b. sentence
   c. dependent clause
   d. noun

17. My brand new dog barks. This is an example of a(n) _____.
   a. phrase
   b. dependent clause
   c. main clause
   d. incomplete sentence

18. Robyn read the book that had 700 pages. What is the dependent clause in this sentence?
   a. that had 700 pages
   b. Robyn read the book
   c. Robyn read
   d. seven hundred pages

19. Which of these is a main clause?
   a. Jerry had a car.
   b. that had a back seat
   c. that had a stereo
   d. that Luis painted for him.

20. Which of these shows a dependent clause?
   a. Justin wore a helmet.
   b. Franco made a scarf.
   c. Gloria wore mittens.
   d. that Jason wanted to wear it

E. ➤ Writing *(20 points)*

> **Writing Prompt** Write a speech that persuades people in your neighborhood to change something. Explain why the change is needed.

VISIONS B Assessment Program • Copyright © Heinle

Name _____ Date _____

Grade

QUIZ Unit 6 • Chapter 4

A. ➤ Vocabulary: Choose the correct answer. *(24 points: 4 points each)*

1. A word that describes a noun is called a(n) _____.
   a. adjective
   b. verb
   c. pronoun
   d. adverb

2. We flew by a large lake. The adjective in this sentence is _____.
   a. flew
   b. lake
   c. large
   d. we

3. You have the correct answer. The adjective in this sentence is _____.
   a. you
   b. answer
   c. have
   d. correct

4. The beautiful necklace was on her dresser. The adjective in this sentence is _____.
   a. necklace
   b. beautiful
   c. dresser
   d. was

5. Political parties <u>nominate</u> candidates. <u>Nominate</u> means to _____.
   a. search for
   b. choose to run for election
   c. speak to
   d. write to

6. Mario was <u>elected</u> president of our class. <u>Elected</u> means _____.
   a. chosen to be
   b. called on
   c. greeted
   d. found

B. ➤ Text Structure/Elements of Literature: Read and choose the correct answer. *(16 points: 4 points each)*

"Mr. Sam Levitz"

1   Sam Levitz was born in 1920. He came to America from Russia. He settled in Detroit, where he worked as a bricklayer. After he saved enough money, he opened his own grocery store. The grocery store was profitable. Today, Mr. Levitz owns over 100 stores in the Michigan area. When Sam Levitz came to America from Russia, he probably never dreamed he would be so successful.

7. "Mr. Sam Levitz" is an example of a _____.
   a. realistic adventure story
   b. personal narrative
   c. biography
   d. speech

8. Which word or phrase describes Sam?
   a. hard-working
   b. weak
   c. lazy
   d. angry

9. "Mr. Sam Levitz" tells a story of _____.
   a. fictional characters
   b. folktales
   c. a person's life
   d. fables

10. Which detail is repeated in the biography?
    a. Sam has three children.
    b. Sam is married.
    c. Sam came to America from Russia.
    d. Sam gives to charity.

95

QUIZ Unit 6 • Chapter 4 (continued)

C. ➤ Reading Strategies: Choose the correct answer. *(16 points: 4 points each)*

11. A(n) _____ is something that can be proven.
    a. fact
    b. opinion
    c. feeling
    d. emotion

12. A(n) _____ is a belief that may be true but cannot be proven.
    a. fact
    b. truth
    c. opinion
    d. evidence

13. Mr. Green's test had 20 questions. Tony thought it was hard. Which of these is a fact?
    a. The test had 20 questions.
    b. The test was difficult.
    c. The test was easy.
    d. The test should have been longer.

14. Craig lives on Hudson Street. He thinks it is the best street in his town. Which of these is an opinion?
    a. Craig lives on Hudson Street.
    b. Craig has friends on Hudson Street.
    c. Hudson Street is the only street in town.
    d. Hudson Street is the best street in town.

D. ➤ Grammar/Usage: Choose the correct answer. *(24 points: 4 points each)*

15. The conjunction _____ shows contrast.
    a. yet
    b. and
    c. after
    d. both

16. I would like to go to the game, yet _____. Finish the sentence to show contrast.
    a. I have not finished my homework
    b. I will get my jacket
    c. my brother will come, too
    d. if my parents agree to let me go

17. I read the assigned chapter, yet _____. Finish the sentence to show contrast.
    a. I could go on to the next chapter
    b. I could not answer all of the questions
    c. I finished the chapter
    d. I understood the story

18. I called Linda to say hello, yet _____. Finish the sentence to show contrast.
    a. I called Linda
    b. I said hello
    c. she did not answer the phone
    d. I dialed the phone number

19. The baseball team was talented, yet _____. Finish the sentence to show contrast.
    a. they won every game
    b. they won almost every game
    c. they did not win the championship
    d. they kept winning

20. The sky looked dark, yet _____. Finish the sentence to show contrast.
    a. it was very wet outside
    b. it was not supposed to rain
    c. it was storming
    d. it was raining

E. ➤ Writing *(20 points)*

Writing Prompt Write a biography about someone you know who faced a challenge. Describe how the person solved his or her problem.

VISIONS B Assessment Program • Copyright © Heinle

TEST • Unit 6

A. ➤ Reading

A Letter from Space

My Notes

1   I got an unbelievable interstellar-mail message today! It was from my friend Rosalita Garza. She is away at camp for the summer. She has sent me a few i-mails before, but none was like this one: It was sent *tomorrow!*

2   I could hardly believe my eyes! You know how regular e-mail on the computer has a date on the top. I-mail from outer space has the same thing. But today's date is July 18, 2103. Her i-mail is dated July 19!

3   I am used to i-mail being fast. Even when i-mail comes from all over the galaxy, it is like talking on a videophone here on Earth. The interstellar communication companies all built quantum accelerators at wormhole entrances. These make the messages move faster than the speed of light. But I have never seen one that got to me *before* it was sent!

4   Rosalita is at space camp this summer. Her camp is on the edge of BH-2. That is the smaller of the two black holes that were discovered right here in the Milky Way galaxy. The black holes were found way back when my grandparents were little children. Back then, my grandfather says, "space camp" meant going to Cape Canaveral to learn about astronauts.

5   Grandpa is talking about a time so long ago that people had only telephones and e-mail. Even when people moved to other planets, they could only use light or radio waves to communicate. A simple conversation took hours or even days! Once i-mail was invented, it got a lot easier. Now, i-mail is faster than regular e-mail.

6   Of course, even when Mama and Papa were children, it would have taken Rosalita more than 1,000 years to get to BH-2. But she rode a near-light-speed ship through a wormhole. Wormholes are the natural tunnels that connect parts of the universe. Wormholes cross through space and time. Rosalita got to camp in just two weeks.

7   Rosalita's message was that she was going to the very edge of the black hole. She went right to the line that's called the *event horizon*. On the other side, nothing can escape the pull of the black hole's gravity, not even light! It seems dangerous to me, but scientists are at the event horizon every day. Rosalita does not seem scared at all. Her i-mail says she is sending it right from the event horizon to see what will happen.

8   I can tell her what happened! Her i-mail got to me *before* she sent it! I guess this proves the theory that time moves backward in a black hole!

TEST • Unit 6 *(continued)*

B. ➤ Reading Comprehension: Choose the correct answer. *(20 points: 2 points each)*

1. The i-mail in "A Letter from Space" was sent by _____.
   a. Grandpa
   b. Rosalita Garza
   c. Mama
   d. Papa

2. Why did the i-mail arrive before it was written?
   a. because the message was sent from the edge of a black hole
   b. because the message was sent from outer space
   c. because the message was sent from summer camp
   d. because the narrator read the date wrong

3. The "i" in i-mail stands for _____.
   a. inside
   b. into
   c. interstellar
   d. intercom

4. The main idea of "A Letter from Space" is that _____.
   a. space camps of the future will be different
   b. i-mail is better than e-mail
   c. time changes in a black hole
   d. Rosalita enjoys conducting experiments

5. From the story, we can infer that Rosalita is _____.
   a. very far away from Earth
   b. on Earth's moon
   c. on Mars
   d. visiting the mountains

6. In "A Letter from Space," i-mail is most like _____.
   a. e-mail
   b. telephones
   c. letters
   d. cameras

7. After reading "A Letter from Space," you can conclude that the author's purpose is to _____.
   a. give factual information about space travel
   b. tell the biography of Rosalita Garza
   c. entertain you with a fantasy about the future
   d. tell a true story about space travel

8. The picture in the reading shows _____.
   a. people looking into space at night
   b. how people travel on Earth
   c. how fast a spaceship can travel
   d. people singing at night

9. In what year does "A Letter from Space" happen?
   a. the present day
   b. 2013
   c. 2103
   d. 2301

10. I got an <u>unbelievable</u> interstellar-mail message today! Why does the narrator describe the message as <u>unbelievable</u>?
   a. because interstellar mail is so amazing
   b. because the message was from Rosalita Garza
   c. because the message came from outer space
   d. because the date on the message was the next day's date

TEST • Unit 6 (continued)

C. ➤ Reading Strategies: Choose the correct answer. *(10 points: 2 points each)*

11. "A Letter from Space" is easier to understand if you use your prior knowledge in _____.
    a. math
    b. social studies
    c. science
    d. music

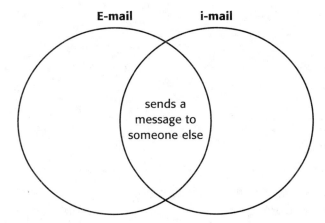

E-mail   **i-mail**

sends a message to someone else

12. Use the Venn Diagram to compare and contrast. Based on the text and the Venn Diagram, you can conclude that e-mail and i-mail _____.
    a. can be made with things found in your home
    b. are letters from the long ago
    c. are tools used to solve science problems
    d. help people to communicate

13. Which of the following sentences is an opinion?
    a. Her i-mail got to me before she sent it.
    b. Rosalita is at space camp this summer.
    c. Rosalita does not seem scared at all.
    d. These make the messages move faster than the speed of light.

14. Based on the story, which of the following is a correct mental image of a black hole?
    a. a place in space that has no light
    b. a huge star, bigger than the sun
    c. a deep hole in the ground
    d. a tunnel that connects parts of the universe

15. Which of the following is the correct sequence of events for "A Letter from Space"?
    a. Rosalita visits the black hole, she goes to camp, she sends an i-mail
    b. Rosalita goes to camp, she comes home again, she visits the black hole
    c. Rosalita sends an i-mail, she visits the black hole, she goes to camp
    d. Rosalita goes to camp, she visits the black hole, she sends an i-mail

D. ➤ Elements of Literature: Choose the correct answer. *(10 points: 2 points each)*

16. Which word best describes the mood of "A Letter from Space"?
    a. sad
    b. angry
    c. worried
    d. excited

17. From details in the story, the reader can assume that Rosalita is _____.
    a. someone who does not like space
    b. adventurous and brave
    c. an experienced scientist
    d. the narrator of the story

18. Who is the story mostly about?
    a. Rosalita
    b. Grandpa
    c. Papa
    d. Mama

TEST • Unit 6 (continued)

19. "A Letter from Space" is a _____.
    a. biography
    b. speech
    c. newspaper article
    d. science fiction story

20. The purpose of "A Letter from Space" is to _____.
    a. inspire the reader to invent i-mail
    b. entertain the reader with a science fiction tale
    c. inform the reader about life in the past
    d. persuade the reader to go to space camp

E. ➤ Vocabulary: Choose the correct answer. *(10 points: 2 points each)*

> **gravity** /'grævəti/ *n.* **1** a natural force pulling objects to the ground **2** seriousness, severity **3** a person's serious attitude or behavior **4** being heavy

21. Look at this dictionary entry. Which meaning matches the meaning of gravity in paragraph 7?
    a. 1
    b. 2
    c. 3
    d. 4

22. Which of the following underlined words is an adjective?
    a. The black holes were found way back when my grandparents were little children.
    b. The black holes were found way back when my grandparents were little children.
    c. The black holes were found way back when my grandparents were little children.
    d. The black holes were found way back when my grandparents were little children.

23. The prefix *un-* in the word unbelievable means _____.
    a. very
    b. again
    c. not
    d. almost

24. Based on the context of paragraph 3, interstellar means _____.
    a. between the stars
    b. on Earth
    c. overseas
    d. in the cellar

25. They saw the sun come up over the horizon. A synonym for horizon is _____.
    a. door
    b. window
    c. edge
    d. building

F. ➤ Grammar/Usage: Choose the correct answer. *(10 points: 2 points each)*

26. Which sentence is correctly punctuated?
    a. My dog a terrier, is named Nugget.
    b. My dog, a terrier, is named Nugget.
    c. My dog a terrier is named Nugget.
    d. My dog, a terrier is named Nugget.

27. Which sentence is correctly punctuated?
    a. He was tired yet he stayed up late.
    b. The runner stumbled, twice yet she won the race.
    c. He is only two years old, yet he can count to 100.
    d. Penguins, have wings yet they cannot fly.

VISIONS B Assessment Program • Copyright © Heinle

TEST • Unit 6 (continued)

28. Which underlined group of words is a dependent clause?
  a. Monday is <u>the day that I begin</u> my vacation.
  b. <u>Monday is the day</u> that I begin my vacation.
  c. Monday is the day that I <u>begin my vacation.</u>
  d. <u>Monday</u> is the day <u>that I begin my vacation.</u>

29. Which sentence uses the past perfect tense?
  a. She felt much happier than she had been before.
  b. She was happier than before.
  c. She felt much happier.
  d. She felt much happier than before the other day.

30. Eddie, my best friend, is meeting Leo at the library in five minutes. This sentence shows an example of a(n) _____.
  a. dialogue
  b. question mark
  c. pronoun
  d. appositive

G. ➤ Writing Conventions: Choose the correct answer. *(10 points: 2 points each)*

31. Which sentence is capitalized correctly?
  a. When Rosalita returns from the Milky way, we will celebrate.
  b. When Rosalita returns from the milky way, we will celebrate.
  c. When rosalita returns from the Milky Way, we will celebrate.
  d. When Rosalita returns from the Milky Way, we will celebrate.

32. Which sentence is correctly punctuated?
  a. Rosalita, my seventh grade friend is away at space camp.
  b. Rosalita, my seventh grade friend, is away at space camp.
  c. Rosalita my seventh grade friend is away at space camp.
  d. Rosalita my seventh grade friend, is away at space camp.

33. Which sentence is correctly punctuated?
  a. Rosalita wrote the i-mail that I received.
  b. Rosalita, wrote the i-mail, that I received.
  c. Rosalita, wrote the i-mail that I received.
  d. Rosalita wrote the i-mail, that, I received.

34 Which underlined word is correct?
  a. In this story, handwritten letters are <u>imnecessary.</u>
  b. <u>In this story,</u> handwritten letters are <u>unnecessary.</u>
  c. <u>In this story,</u> handwritten letters are <u>innecessary.</u>
  d. In this story, handwritten letters are <u>unecessary.</u>

35. Which underlined word is correct?
  a. In a black hole, the change in time is <u>unknown</u>.
  b. In a black hole, the change in time is <u>imknown</u>.
  c. In a black hole, the change in time is <u>knowning</u>.
  d. In a black hole, the change in time is <u>unnknowable</u>.

TEST • Unit 6 (continued)

H. ➤ **Editing:** Read and choose the correct answer. *(10 points: 2 points each)*

Eva

1 Eva a girl in seventh grade, is quite amazing.
2 Her enjoys space travel.
3 She always interested in seeing space.
4 Her friends all like her.
5 They say that they admire here.
6 She is as brave of a lion, everyone says.

---

36. What change should you make to sentence 1?
   a. change *Eva* to *eva*
   b. add a comma after *Eva*
   c. add a comma after *is*
   d. change quite to *quitely*

37. What change should you make to sentence 2?
   a. change *Her* to *She*
   b. change *enjoys* to *enjoy*
   c. add a comma after *space*
   d. make no change

38. Sentence 3 is best written _____.
   a. Seeing outer space was always an interest of Rosalita's
   b. She has always been interested in seeing outer space
   c. Rosalita wanted to see outer space
   d. Rosalita is interested in outer space

39. What change should you make to sentence 5?
   a. change *They* to *Them*
   b. change *say* to *says*
   c. change *here* to *her*
   d. make no change

40. What change should you make to sentence 6?
   a. change *is* to *be*
   b. change *as* to *like*
   c. change *of* to *as*
   d. make no change

I. ➤ **Writing** *(20 points)*

Writing Prompt Write three paragraphs to explain what happens when Rosalita returns to Earth from space camp. Give the story an ending. Use the Planning Guide to help you write.

Planning Guide
❏ Describe your characters' actions and reactions with adjectives.
❏ Be certain that the narrator remains the same.
❏ Use past perfect tense when appropriate.

VISIONS B Assessment Program • Copyright © Heinle

END-OF-BOOK EXAM

A. ➤ Reading

Polio

1   It is hard to believe that just 60 years ago, polio was a very frightening disease. This disease had been dreaded for thousands of years. In the 1940s, parents were almost in a panic about it.

2   Part of the reason was the common name for polio. It was called "infantile paralysis." Polio struck children, paralyzing parts of their bodies so they could never move them again. Some victims were unable to breathe on their own. To get air, they had to live in what were called "iron lungs."

3   Researchers hunted for years to find something that would prevent polio. Finally, in 1947, a team led by Dr. John Enders found a way to grow the polio virus in test tubes. Then, it was just a matter of time before a vaccine was created. Two doctors, Jonas Salk and Albert Sabin, were almost in a race to discover the polio vaccine.

4   If it was a race, Dr. Salk won. His vaccine was given as a shot. In 1954, the United States began giving the Salk vaccine to every child in the country. Dr. Sabin's vaccine arrived a couple of years later. It was given as a drop of liquid on a sugar cube. Together, the doctors brought the disease under control.

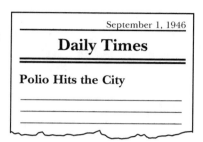

September 1, 1946

Daily Times

Polio Hits the City

My Notes

My Teacher

1   I think of my fifth-grade teacher almost every day. Mr. Rodriguez had been a victim of polio. He must have been one of the last children in the United States to suffer from the disease.

2   Although he did not wear a brace, Mr. Rodriguez walked with a limp. His left foot turned far to the inside. He could not use his left arm below the elbow, but Mr. Rodriguez played softball with us at recess. He held the bat high up under his left arm. Then, he threw the ball high into the air with his right hand. He quickly grabbed the bat in his right hand to hit the falling, spinning ball.

3   I learned many things from Mr. Rodriguez that year. He turned books into shooting stars, taking us to another world. However, the most important lesson he taught me came one day when I held the door for him. I looked at his left arm. "This?" he said, looking at his arm. "This is nothing I cannot overcome."

4   Now I am an adult. Every problem I face, small or large, brings Mr. Rodriguez to my mind. Each time, I see his face and tell myself, "This is nothing I cannot overcome." And so far, Mr. Rodriguez has been right every time.

END-OF-BOOK EXAM (continued)

B. ➤ **Reading Comprehension:** Choose the correct answer. *(20 points: 2 points each)*

1. According to "Polio," when were parents almost in a panic about polio?
   a. the 1800s
   b. the 1920s
   c. the 1940s
   d. today

2. In "My Teacher," how did Mr. Rodriguez hit a softball?
   a. He grabbed the bat with his right hand and hit the ball one-handed.
   b. He hit the ball like everyone else.
   c. Mr. Rodriguez was unable to hit a softball.
   d. He grabbed the bat with both hands and hit the ball.

3. In "Polio," what made it just a matter of time before a polio vaccine was discovered?
   a. Researchers had been looking for a vaccine for a long time.
   b. More doctors were beginning to search for a vaccine.
   c. In 1954, different vaccines were being tested.
   d. In 1947, a team led by Dr. John Enders found a way to grow the polio virus in a test tube.

4. Who won the "race" to find a polio vaccine?
   a. Dr. John Enders
   b. Dr. Albert Sabin
   c. Mr. Rodriguez
   d. Dr. Jonas Salk

5. Why does the narrator of "My Teacher" think Mr. Rodriguez is "right every time"?
   a. Because the narrator did not know anyone else who had caught polio.
   b. Because the narrator has overcome obstacles by thinking of Mr. Rodriguez.
   c. Because Mr. Rodriguez never makes mistakes.
   d. Because Mr. Rodriguez told the narrator so.

6. According to "Polio," when did children in the United States begin to be vaccinated against polio?
   a. 1947
   b. 1950
   c. 1952
   d. 1954

7. Why does the narrator of "My Teacher" think of Mr. Rodriguez when he has a problem?
   a. Because the narrator liked Mr. Rodriguez and thinks of him often.
   b. Because Mr. Rodriguez taught the narrator a song to sing whenever he had a problem.
   c. Because the narrator is reminded that he can overcome his problems, just as Mr. Rodriguez did.
   d. Because the narrator thought Mr. Rodriguez was funny.

8. In "Polio," what caused some children with polio to live in "iron lungs"?
   a. They were unable to breathe on their own.
   b. They had no lungs of their own.
   c. The "iron lungs" was the name of their homes.
   d. The "iron lungs" was the name of Dr. Sabin's cure.

END-OF-BOOK EXAM (continued)

9. "Polio" and "My Teacher" both show how polio _____.
   a. is still a major concern today
   b. affected the lives of people
   c. can be researched
   d. is spreading all over the world

10. In "My Teacher," you can infer that the narrator _____.
    a. knew a lot about polio
    b. wanted to be a doctor
    c. did not like recess
    d. learned a lesson from Mr. Rodriguez

C. ➤ Reading Strategies: Choose the correct answer. *(10 points: 2 points each)*

11. In what way are "Polio" and "My Teacher" alike?
    a. They both are written with dialogue and action.
    b. They both tell about triumphs over polio.
    c. They both talk about Dr. Jonas Salk.
    d. They both tell why people are vaccinated against polio.

12. What is the main idea of "My Teacher"?
    a. People used to catch polio in the United States.
    b. Mr. Rodriguez was unlucky.
    c. A person can overcome obstacles.
    d. A person can hit a softball with just one hand.

13. In paragraph 3 of "Polio," what can you infer about how Dr. Salk and Dr. Sabin felt about each other?
    a. They were competing against each other.
    b. They were close friends.
    c. They liked working together.
    d. They did not know each other.

14. What does Mr. Rodriguez's dialogue in paragraph 3 of "My Teacher" tell you about him?
    a. Mr. Rodriguez feels sorry for himself.
    b. Mr. Rodriguez is a funny man who loves to tell jokes.
    c. Mr. Rodriguez will not let his disability prevent him from normal activity.
    d. Mr. Rodriguez has many problems.

15. Based on "Polio," what is the correct chronology of the discovery of a polio vaccine?
    a. In 1960, children in the United States were being vaccinated against polio.
    b. In 1947, the first vaccine was made. In 1954, a vaccine was widely used. Before 1960, two vaccines were used together.
    c. In 1952, the first vaccine was created. In 1954, a vaccine was widely used. Before 1960, two vaccines were used together.
    d. In 1947, the first major step toward a vaccine was made. In 1954, a vaccine was widely used.

D. ➤ Elements of Literature: Choose the correct answer. *(10 points: 2 points each)*

16. How do you know that "My Teacher" is written in the first-person point of view?
    a. The narrator is talking about someone else.
    b. The narrator uses the pronouns I, we, and our.
    c. A character in the story is named Mr. Rodriguez.
    d. Mr. Rodriguez has dialogue in the story.

17. From the writing style of "Polio," it is clear that the author's purpose is to _____.
    a. fill the reader with suspense
    b. tell the reader a simple news story
    c. give the reader information about a medical miracle
    d. invite the reader to wonder about how medical treatments are found

END-OF-BOOK EXAM (continued)

18. Which word best describes the mood in "Polio?"
    a. anger
    b. sadness
    c. confusion
    d. wonder

19. He turned books into shooting stars, taking us to another world. What is being compared in this metaphor from "My Teacher"?
    a. Mr. Rodriguez to his students
    b. stars to another world
    c. books to shooting stars
    d. Mr. Rodriguez to another world

20. He quickly grabbed the bat in his right hand to hit the falling, spinning ball. Which words are used to make the sentence more vivid?
    a. in his
    b. falling, spinning
    c. right hand
    d. hit the

E. ➤ Vocabulary: Choose the correct answer. (10 points: 2 points each)

21. The word infantile comes from the Latin word *infans*. *Infans* means "a person who is not yet able to speak." Infantile means ____.
    a. relating to silence
    b. relating to a small child or baby
    c. relating to people
    d. relating to illness

22. Researchers hunted for years to find something that would prevent polio. In this sentence, hunted means ____.
    a. looked
    b. found
    c. heard
    d. made

23. The words virus and polio are related to the word ____.
    a. disease
    b. year
    c. cause
    d. person

24. He was able to overcome the disease. A synonym for overcome is ____.
    a. beat
    b. lose
    c. disappear
    d. forget

25. The disease had been dreaded for thousands of years. Dreaded means ____.
    a. a period of time
    b. an illness
    c. dangerous
    d. greatly feared

F. ➤ Grammar/Usage: Choose the correct answer. (10 points: 2 points each)

26. The geese had flown south for the winter. How can you change had flown into the past continuous tense?
    a. will fly
    b. were flying
    c. are flying
    d. would have flown

27. Which sentence is correct?
    a. He play the piano very well.
    b. It look like it is going to rain today.
    c. She talks on the phone constantly.
    d. He think he can solve the puzzle.

VISIONS B Assessment Program • Copyright © Heinle

END-OF-BOOK EXAM (continued)

28. Which underlined words are a prepositional phrase?
  a. We found the book that he had lost <u>under the bed</u>.
  b. We found the book <u>that he had lost</u> under the bed.
  c. <u>We found the book</u> that he had lost under the bed.
  d. We found the <u>book that he had lost</u> under the bed.

29. Which sentence is in the present perfect tense?
  a. We took the train to San Francisco.
  b. We have taken the train to San Francisco.
  c. We take the train to San Francisco.
  d. We will take the train to San Francisco.

30. When the boys found the leather wallet, <u>it</u> contained no identification. It refers to _____.
  a. boys
  b. identification
  c. leather
  d. wallet

G. ➤ Writing Conventions: Choose the correct answer. *(10 points: 2 points each)*

31. Which sentence below is punctuated correctly?
  a. Although we were tired we continued to hike.
  b. Later that day the wind began to blow.
  c. When the whistle blew, the player dropped the ball.
  d. They enjoyed the amusement park but it was crowded.

32. Which sentence shows the correct use of capital letters?
  a. Mother asked Dr. Jones if I could go to New York city with a broken arm.
  b. Mother asked dr. Jones if I could go to New York City with a broken arm.
  c. mother asked Dr. Jones if I could go to New York City with a broken arm.
  d. Mother asked Dr. Jones if I could go to New York City with a broken arm.

33. All of the _____ will go to the park. Which word correctly completes the sentence?
  a. child
  b. children
  c. childs
  d. childrens

34. Which underlined word is spelled correctly?
  a. The police <u>chief</u> spoke to the reporter.
  b. The police <u>cheif</u> spoke to the reporter.
  c. The police <u>cheef</u> spoke to the reporter.
  d. The police <u>cheaf</u> spoke to the reporter.

35. Which sentence correctly uses apostrophes to show possession?
  a. The dog hurt it's paw when Tom's bike fell over.
  b. The dog hurt its paw when Toms' bike fell over.
  c. The dog hurt its paw when Tom's bike fell over.
  d. The dog hurt its' paw when Tom's bike fell over.

END-OF-BOOK EXAM (continued)

H. ➤ **Editing:** Read and choose the correct answer. *(10 points: 2 points each)*

Polio Today

1 Polio is now unnown in the United States.

2 The last new case was in 1979.

3 It is still presented in other parts of the world.

4 The World health Organization is trying to get rid of the disease whenever it still exists.

5 It are trying to get vaccines to small children everywhere.

6 The disease infects person in 50 countries worldwide.

---

36. What change should you make to sentence 1?
a. change *Polio* to *polio*
b. change *unnown* to *unknown*
c. change *United* to *united*
d. change *States* to *states*

37. In sentence 3, presented should be changed to _____.
a. presenter
b. presenting
c. presentiment
d. present

38. In sentence 4, the World health Organization should be changed to _____.
a. world health organization
b. World Health Organization
c. WORLD HEALTH ORGANIZATION
d. world Health organization

39. What change should you make to sentence 5?
a. change *it* to *they*
b. change *trying* to *try*
c. change *everywhere* to *anywhere*
d. make no change

40. What change should you make to sentence 6?
a. change *disease* to *diseases*
b. change *person* to *people*
c. change *countries* to *country*
d. make no change

I. ➤ **Writing** *(20 points)*

Writing Prompt Write a five-paragraph essay to compare and contrast "Polio" and "My Teacher." Use the Planning Guide to help you write.

Planning Guide
❑ Show how the two readings are alike.
❑ Show how the two readings are different.
❑ Include important information that makes each reading stand out from the other.
❑ When you finish writing, check your spelling.

VISIONS B Assessment Program • Copyright © Heinle

Answer Key

Diagnostic Test

1. a	13. a	25. b
2. c	14. d	26. c
3. c	15. d	27. a
4. b	16. d	28. a
5. b	17. a	29. b
6. c	18. b	30. d
7. b	19. b	31. b
8. b	20. c	32. c
9. c	21. d	33. a
10. a	22. b	34. d
11. a	23. c	35. a
12. b	24. d	

Writing: Answers will vary.

36. a	38. d	40. d
37. c	39. c	

Unit 1
Chapter 1 Quiz

A. Vocabulary

1. c	3. c	5. c
2. b	4. d	6. b

B. Text Structure/Elements of Literature

7. c	10. c	12. d
8. c	11. b	13. a
9. c		

C. Reading Strategies

14. b	15. a	16. b

D. Grammar/Usage

17. d	19. d
18. c	20. b

E. Writing
Answers will vary.

Unit 1
Chapter 2 Quiz

A. Vocabulary

1. b	3. c	5. b
2. a	4. a	6. d

B. Text Structure/Elements of Literature

7. a	10. a	13. c
8. d	11. a	14. c
9. b	12. d	

C. Reading Strategies

15. c	16. b	17. d

D. Grammar/Usage

18. b	19. d	20. a

E. Writing
Answers will vary.

Unit 1
Chapter 3 Quiz

A. Vocabulary

1. b	3. c	5. a
2. c	4. b	6. c

B. Text Structure/Elements of Literature

7. a	10. a	12. a
8. a	11. d	13. d
9. d		

C. Reading Strategies

14. d	15. b	16. a

D. Grammar/Usage

17. a	19. d
18. b	20. b

E. Writing
Answers will vary.

Unit 1
Chapter 4 Quiz

A. Vocabulary

1. d	3. c	5. b
2. a	4. b	6. c

B. Text Structure/Elements of Literature

7. d	9. b	11. c
8. b	10. a	12. b

C. Reading Strategies

13. b	14. d	15. d

D. Grammar/Usage

16. c	18. a	20. a
17. a	19. b	

E. Writing
Answers will vary.

Unit 1
Chapter 5 Quiz

A. Vocabulary

1. b	4. d	7. b
2. c	5. b	8. a
3. a	6. b	

B. Text Structure/Elements of Literature

9. c	11. b
10. d	12. a

C. Reading Strategies

13. b	15. d
14. a	16. c

D. Grammar/Usage

17. d	19. d
18. b	20. b

E. Writing
Answers will vary.

Unit 1 Test

B. Reading Comprehension

1. a	5. b	9. a
2. c	6. d	10. d
3. c	7. b	
4. d	8. a	

C. Reading Strategies

11. c	13. b	15. a
12. c	14. d	

D. Elements of Literature

16. b	18. a	20. a
17. d	19. b	

E. Vocabulary

21. c	23. d	25. c
22. b	24. d	

F. Grammar/Usage

26. c	28. a	30. a
27. a	29. d	

G. Writing Conventions

31. b	33. a	35. c
32. c	34. d	

H. Editing
36. a   38. b   40. c
37. c   39. b

I. Writing
Answers will vary.

Unit 2
Chapter 1 Quiz

A. Vocabulary
1. a   3. b   5. a
2. d   4. c   6. b

B. Text Structure/Elements of Literature
7. d   9. c   11. c
8. a   10. b

C. Reading Strategies
12. b   13. b   14. a

D. Grammar/Usage
15. c   17. b   19. a
16. c   18. c   20. a

E. Writing
Answers will vary.

Unit 2
Chapter 2 Quiz

A. Vocabulary
1. b   4. d   7. c
2. a   5. c
3. c   6. b

B. Text Structure/Elements of Literature
8. a   10. a
9. c   11. d

C. Reading Strategies
12. c   14. d
13. a   15. a

D. Grammar/Usage
16. d   18. b   20. c
17. a   19. d

E. Writing
Answers will vary.

Unit 2
Chapter 3 Quiz

A. Vocabulary
1. b   3. a   5. d
2. c   4. d   6. d

B. Text Structure/Elements of Literature
7. b   9. b   11. d
8. a   10. c   12. b

C. Reading Strategies
13. c   15. b
14. b   16. d

D. Grammar/Usage
17. b   19. b
18. a   20. a

E. Writing
Answers will vary.

Unit 2
Chapter 4 Quiz

A. Vocabulary
1. d   4. c   7. d
2. a   5. b   8. d
3. c   6. a

B. Text Structure/Elements of Literature
9. c   11. c
10. b   12. d

C. Reading Strategies
13. d   15. c
14. d   16. d

D. Grammar/Usage
17. c   19. d
18. b   20. d

E. Writing
Answers will vary.

Unit 2
Chapter 5 Quiz

A. Vocabulary
1. d   3. b   5. b
2. a   4. c   6. a

B. Text Structure/Elements of Literature
7. b   9. a   11. d
8. b   10. c

C. Reading Strategies
12. a   14. d
13. d   15. d

D. Grammar/Usage
16. b   18. d   20. b
17. b   19. c

E. Writing
Answers will vary.

Unit 2 Test

B. Reading Comprehension
1. a   5. d   9. b
2. c   6. b   10. c
3. b   7. b
4. c   8. d

C. Reading Strategies
11. b   13. a   15. b
12. a   14. c

D. Elements of Literature
16. d   18. b   20. c
17. b   19. d

E. Vocabulary
21. b   23. b   25. d
22. a   24. d

F. Grammar/Usage
26. c   28. a   30. a
27. d   29. b

G. Writing Conventions
31. c   33. d   35. d
32. c   34. b

H. Editing
36. c   38. b   40. d
37. a   39. c

I. Writing
Answers will vary.

Unit 3
Chapter 1 Quiz

A. Vocabulary
1. a   3. d   5. b
2. a   4. d   6. a

VISIONS B Assessment Program • Copyright © Heinle

B. Text Structure/Elements of Literature

7. c 9. c 11. a
8. d 10. a 12. c

C. Reading Strategies

13. a 14. b 15. b

D. Grammar/Usage

16. d 19. b
17. d 20. c
18. c

E. Writing
Answers will vary.

Unit 3
Chapter 2 Quiz

A. Vocabulary

1. d 4. c 7. a
2. a 5. a 8. d
3. b 6. d

B. Text Structure/Elements of Literature

9. d 11. b 13. a
10. c 12. b 14. c

C. Reading Strategies

15. a 16. a 17. b

D. Grammar/Usage

18. c 19. a 20. b

E. Writing
Answers will vary.

Unit 3
Chapter 3 Quiz

A. Vocabulary

1. c 3. a 5. b
2. b 4. b 6. b

B. Text Structure/Elements of Literature

7. d 9. c 11. c
8. b 10. a 12. c

C. Reading Strategies

13. a 14. b 15. c

D. Grammar/Usage

16. a 18. a 20. c
17. c 19. c

E. Writing
Answers will vary.

Unit 3
Chapter 4 Quiz

A. Vocabulary

1. a 3. a 5. b
2. d 4. a 6. c

B. Text Structure/Elements of Literature

7. b 9. c 11. d
8. d 10. b 12. c

C. Reading Strategies

13. a 14. b 15. a

D. Grammar/Usage

16. a 18. a 20. b
17. c 19. c

E. Writing
Answers will vary.

Unit 3
Chapter 5 Quiz

A. Vocabulary

1. b 3. b 5. d
2. a 4. b 6. c

B. Text Structure/Elements of Literature

7. b 9. d 11. b
8. a 10. a 12. b

C. Reading Strategies

13. b 14. c 15. c

D. Grammar/Usage

16. d 18. a 20. d
17. b 19. b

E. Writing
Answers will vary.

Unit 3 Test

B. Reading Comprehension

1. a 5. d 9. b
2. b 6. b 10. a
3. c 7. c
4. b 8. d

C. Reading Strategies

11. a 13. d 15. b
12. b 14. c

D. Elements of Literature

16. c 18. d 20. b
17. b 19. a

E. Vocabulary

21. a 23. c 25. a
22. b 24. b

F. Grammar/Usage

26. d 28. c 30. b
27. b 29. b

G. Writing Conventions

31. d 33. c 35. d
32. a 34. b

H. Editing

36. c 38. a 40. a
37. c 39. b

I. Writing
Answers will vary.

Mid-Book Exam

B. Reading Comprehension

1. c 5. b 9. b
2. a 6. d 10. a
3. c 7. d
4. d 8. c

C. Reading Strategies

11. b 13. a 15. c
12. c 14. c

D. Elements of Literature

16. b 18. d 20. d
17. c 19. c

E. Vocabulary

21. b 23. d 25. d
22. a 24. a

F. Grammar/Usage

26. d 28. c 30. b
27. a 29. a

G. Writing Conventions

31. b 33. c 35. b
32. b 34. d

H. Editing

36. c 38. c 40. b
37. a 39. c

I. Writing
Answers will vary.

Unit 4
Chapter 1 Quiz

A. Vocabulary
1. b   3. b   5. b
2. c   4. d   6. a

B. Text Structure/Elements of Literature
7. b   10. a   13. d
8. c   11. d
9. c   12. b

C. Reading Strategies
14. a   16. b
15. b   17. c

D. Grammar/Usage
18. a   19. c   20. d

E. Writing
Answers will vary.

Unit 4
Chapter 2 Quiz

A. Vocabulary
1. d   3. b   5. c
2. a   4. d

B. Text Structure/Elements of Literature
6. b   9. c   12. b
7. a   10. a
8. d   11. d

C. Reading Strategies
13. c   15. b
14. a   16. c

D. Grammar/Usage
17. d   19. b
18. b   20. a

E. Writing
Answers will vary.

Unit 4
Chapter 3 Quiz

A. Vocabulary
1. b   3. a   5. c
2. d   4. b   6. c

B. Text Structure/Elements of Literature
7. d   9. a   11. d
8. b   10. b   12. c

C. Reading Strategies
13. d   15. a
14. d   16. c

D. Grammar/Usage
17. b   19. a
18. c   20. b

E. Writing
Answers will vary.

Unit 4
Chapter 4 Quiz

A. Vocabulary
1. b   3. a   5. b
2. d   4. c   6. a

B. Text Structure/Elements of Literature
7. b   10. d   13. c
8. a   11. d   14. b
9. c   12. b

C. Reading Strategies
15. a   16. c   17. d

D. Grammar/Usage
18. b   19. d   20. a

E. Writing
Answers will vary.

Unit 4 Test

B. Reading Comprehension
1. b   5. b   9. d
2. d   6. a   10. b
3. a   7. a
4. c   8. a

C. Reading Strategies
11. d   13. c   15. b
12. a   14. a

D. Elements of Literature
16. a   18. b   20. c
17. b   19. a

E. Vocabulary
21. b   23. d   25. c
22. b   24. c

F. Grammar/Usage
26. d   28. a   30. d
27. c   29. c

G. Writing Conventions
31. b   33. d   35. b
32. c   34. a

H. Editing
36. a   38. a   40. c
37. c   39. c

I. Writing
Answers will vary.

Unit 5
Chapter 1 Quiz

A. Vocabulary
1. b   3. b   5. b
2. c   4. a   6. d

B. Text Structure/Elements of Literature
7. c   10. d   13. a
8. c   11. b
9. b   12. b

C. Reading Strategies
14. b   16. d
15. a   17. c

D. Grammar/Usage
18. b   19. c   20. b

E. Writing
Answers will vary.

Unit 5
Chapter 2 Quiz

A. Vocabulary
1. c   3. b   5. c
2. b   4. c   6. b

VISIONS B Assessment Program • Copyright © Heinle

B. Text Structure/Elements of Literature

7. d	10. a	13. a
8. c	11. b	
9. b	12. b	

C. Reading Strategies

14. a	16. d
15. d	17. c

D. Grammar/Usage

18. c	19. a	20. b

E. Writing
Answers will vary.

Unit 5 Chapter 3 Quiz

A. Vocabulary

1. c	3. c	5. b
2. b	4. a	6. b

B. Text Structure/Elements of Literature

7. c	10. a	13. c
8. c	11. c	
9. b	12. a	

C. Reading Strategies

14. b	16. a
15. d	17. c

D. Grammar/Usage

18. b	19. b	20. c

E. Writing
Answers will vary.

Unit 5 Chapter 4 Quiz

A. Vocabulary

1. a	3. c	5. d
2. c	4. d	6. c

B. Text Structure/Elements of Literature

7. b	10. b	13. b
8. b	11. b	
9. d	12. b	

C. Reading Strategies

14. b	16. b
15. d	17. c

D. Grammar/Usage

18. b	19. a	20. a

E. Writing
Answers will vary.

Unit 5 Test

B. Reading Comprehension

1. a	5. d	9. c
2. a	6. a	10. b
3. b	7. d	
4. b	8. c	

C. Reading Strategies

11. b	13. b	15. c
12. a	14. d	

D. Elements of Literature

16. a	18. c	20. a
17. c	19. a	

E. Vocabulary

21. d	23. a	25. c
22. b	24. a	

F. Grammar/Usage

26. c	28. a	30. b
27. b	29. a	

G. Writing Conventions

31. b	33. a	35. c
32. c	34. c	

H. Editing

36. b	38. d	40. c
37. a	39. b	

I. Writing
Answers will vary.

Unit 6 Chapter 1 Quiz

A. Vocabulary

1. d	3. b	5. a
2. d	4. a	6. a

B. Text Structure/Elements of Literature

7. c	9. b
8. a	10. a

C. Reading Strategies

11. b	13. c
12. b	14. a

D. Grammar/Usage

15. c	17. c	19. b
16. a	18. a	20. c

E. Writing
Answers will vary.

Unit 6 Chapter 2 Quiz

A. Vocabulary

1. b	3. d	5. d
2. b	4. b	6. a

B. Text Structure/Elements of Literature

7. c	9. c	11. b
8. b	10. d	

C. Reading Strategies

12. b	13. a	14. c

D. Grammar/Usage

15. c	17. c	19. c
16. b	18. b	20. d

E. Writing
Answers will vary.

Unit 6 Chapter 3 Quiz

A. Vocabulary

1. c	3. b	5. c
2. a	4. d	6. a

B. Text Structure/Elements of Literature

7. d	9. c
8. b	10. d

C. Reading Strategies

11. a	13. d
12. a	14. b

D. Grammar/Usage

15. b	17. c	19. a
16. c	18. a	20. d

E. Writing
Answers will vary.

Unit 6
Chapter 4 Quiz

A. Vocabulary

1. a   3. d   5. b
2. c   4. b   6. a

B. Text Structure/Elements of Literature

7. c   9. c
8. a   10. c

C. Reading Strategies

11. a   13. a
12. c   14. d

D. Grammar/Usage

15. a   17. b   19. c
16. a   18. c   20. b

E. Writing

Answers will vary.

Unit 6 Test

B. Reading Comprehension

1. b   5. a   9. c
2. a   6. a   10. d
3. c   7. c
4. c   8. a

C. Reading Strategies

11. c   13. c   15. d
12. d   14. a

D. Elements of Literature

16. d   18. a   20. b
17. b   19. d

E. Vocabulary

21. a   23. c   25. c
22. b   24. a

F. Grammar/Usage

26. b   28. d   30. d
27. c   29. a

G. Writing Conventions

31. d   33. a   35. a
32. b   34. b

H. Editing

36. b   38. b   40. c
37. a   39. c

I. Writing

Answers will vary.

End-of-Book Exam

B. Reading Comprehension

1. c   5. b   9. b
2. a   6. d   10. d
3. d   7. c
4. d   8. a

C. Reading Strategies

11. b   13. a   15. d
12. c   14. c

D. Elements of Literature

16. b   18. d   20. b
17. c   19. c

E. Vocabulary

21. b   23. a   25. d
22. a   24. a

F. Grammar/Usage

26. b   28. a   30. d
27. c   29. b

G. Writing Conventions

31. c   33. b   35. c
32. d   34. a

H. Editing

36. b   38. b   40. b
37. d   39. a

I. Writing

Answers will vary.

VISIONS B Assessment Program • Copyright © Heinle

Name _____ Date _____

📁 Portfolio: Activity Rating and Reflection Sheet

Part I: Rating

Write the name of each activity in your work folder on the left. Think about how much you liked it. Circle one number for each activity.

Unit ____ Activities	I didn't like it.	I liked it a little.	I liked it.	I liked it very much.
_____	1	2	3	4
_____	1	2	3	4
_____	1	2	3	4
_____	1	2	3	4
_____	1	2	3	4
_____	1	2	3	4
_____	1	2	3	4
_____	1	2	3	4

Part II: Reflection

1. My Portfolio choice for Unit ____

I chose to put _____ in my Portfolio because

_____ .

2. How I Learned

I learned best from . . .

____ listening and speaking.   ____ reading.   ____ writing.

I liked working . . .

____ by myself.   ____ with a partner.   ____ with a small group.   ____ with the whole class.

Reading Fluency Chart

How many words did you read in one minute? Color in the graph up to the number of words that you read.

When you read silently, color in the chart with red. When you read orally, color in the chart with blue.

Words per Minute	Key: Silent Reading = Red Oral Reading = Blue																												
180																													
175																													
170																													
165																													
160																													
155																													
150																													
145																													
140																													
135																													
130																													
125																													
120																													
115																													
110																													
105																													
100																													
95																													
90																													
85																													
80																													
75																													
70																													
65																													
60																													
55																													
50																													
45																													
40																													
35																													
30																													
25																													
20																													
15																													
10																													
Reading Exercise	1	2	3	4	5	1	2	3	4	5	1	2	3	4	5	1	2	3	4	1	2	3	4	1	2	3	4
Unit	1					2					3					4				5				6			

VISIONS B Assessment Program • Copyright © Heinle

Responding to Peers' Writing: *EQS*

E: Encourage	*Q*: Question	*S*: Suggestions
• Help your partner recognize what he or she is doing right. • Be specific. Say things like: "I liked the surprise at the end the best." "You used some very interesting words in this sentence." "This poem made me think of my home."	• Ask questions when you would like more information. • Ask questions when something isn't clear. For example: "Why did your grandmother give you that picture?" "What do you mean, 'He went back'? Where did he go?"	• Ask your partner if he or she would like some suggestions. If your partner says "yes," offer suggestions to make the writing better. • Always let your partner choose whether or not to use your ideas. • Don't tell your partner what to do. Instead, make suggestions like: "You might try saying, 'My dog is fat' another way. How about 'My dog looks like a sausage with four legs'?" "What if you changed these two sentences around?"

Read your partner's selection. Use *EQS* to fill in the boxes.

Name _____   Partner's Name _____

E: Encourage	*Q*: Question	*S*: Suggestions

Peer Editing Checklist

Use this checklist to edit your peer's writing.
You may also use it to check your own writing.

Writer's Name _____

Editor's Name _____

1. Is there a title? _____ Yes _____ No

2. Is the first sentence of each paragraph indented? _____ Yes _____ No

3. Does each sentence start with a capital letter? _____ Yes _____ No

4. Does each sentence end with a punctuation mark? _____ Yes _____ No

5. Does each name start with a capital letter? _____ Yes _____ No

6. Write one correct sentence from the paper.

_____

7. Write one sentence that has a mistake.

_____

8. Rewrite the sentence correctly.

_____

Use these editing symbols:	
¶	Start a new paragraph.
∧	Insert a word or words.
Sp	Correct a spelling error.
CAP	Use a capital letter.
lc	Use a lowercase letter.
p	Correct a punctuation error.
exact	Use a more exact word.
?	What does this mean?
∽	Transpose these letters.

VISIONS B Assessment Program • Copyright © Heinle

Name _____

Editor's Checklist

Use this checklist to proofread and revise your writing. Make a check in the box when you have edited your writing for each item. Give this checklist to your teacher with your writing assignment.

Edit for:	Student Check ✔	Teacher Comments	Score

I. Development of Ideas/Content
  A. Is the purpose of my writing clear? ☐
  B. Is my writing focused on the topic I'm writing about? ☐
  C. Did I support my ideas with details, facts, and examples? ☐
  D. Did I write appropriately for my audience? ☐			

II. Organization
  A. Is my writing clear and logical? ☐
  B. Do I have a strong, interesting beginning that gets the reader's attention? ☐
  C. Are my ideas tied together? Do I use transitions? ☐
  D. Do I have a strong ending that ties things together? ☐			

III. Sentence Structure
  A. Are my sentences complete? Do they have a subject and a verb? ☐
  B. Did I make sure I don't have any run-on sentences or fragments? ☐
  C. Did I use different types of sentences—compound and complex? ☐			

IV. Grammar and Usage
  A. Is my writing in the right tense (for example, present or past)? ☐
  B. Did I use subject pronouns and object pronouns correctly—*I/me, he/him, she/her, we/us, they/them?* ☐
  C. Did I use the pronouns *she, her,* or *hers* for women and girls and *he, him,* or *his* for men and boys? ☐
  D. Do my verbs agree with their subjects? Did I use singular verbs with singular subjects and plural verbs with plural subjects? ☐			

VISIONS B Assessment Program • Copyright © Heinle

Editor's Checklist (cont . . .)

Edit for:	Student Check ☑	Teacher Comments	Score

V. Word Choice
    A. Did I choose vivid and exact words? Did I use a thesaurus, glossary, or dictionary to help me choose better words?
    B. Did I eliminate extra words so that my writing is not wordy?
	☐
	
	☐		

VI. Writing Conventions
Form
    A. Did I write my name, the date, and a title on the page?
    B. Did I indent the first line of each paragraph?
    C. Did I include a bibliography and correctly cite any references that I used?
    D. Did I create an attractive computer presentation, or did I use my best handwriting?
 	
Spelling
    E. Did I check the spelling of all words I'm not sure about?
    F. If I wrote my paper on a computer, did I use spell check?
 	
Capitalization
    G. Did I capitalize the names of proper nouns, such as people's names and the names of cities and countries?
    H. Did I start each sentence with a capital letter?
 	
Punctuation
    I. Did I punctuate each sentence with the right mark (., ?, or !)?
    J. Did I put quotation marks around any direct speech?
    K. Did I use apostrophes correctly in contractions and possessives?
	☐
	☐
	☐
	
	☐
	
	☐
	☐
	
	☐
	☐
	
	☐
	☐
	☐		

VII. My Own Criteria
    A.
 	
    B.
 	
    C.
	☐
	
	☐
	
	☐		

VISIONS B Assessment Program • Copyright © Heinle

Name _____

Narrative Checklist

Use this checklist to evaluate your own writing and your classmates' writing.

```
_____ Interesting title

_____ Name

_____ Date
```

Introduction
1. _____ describes the setting
2. _____ introduces the characters
3. _____ introduces the problem or topic

Body
1. _____ describes an event
2. _____ gives details about the event
3. _____ uses sequence to relate events (throughout)

1. _____ describes an event
2. _____ gives details about the event
3. _____ uses strong verbs and vivid adjectives (throughout)

1. _____ brings problem to climax
2. _____ builds suspense for reader
3. _____ uses figurative language so the reader can "see," "taste," "hear," and "feel" the events (throughout)

Conclusion or Resolution
1. _____ restates problem
2. _____ shows how problem is resolved
3. _____ has a strong ending

_____ I used the Editor's Checklist to edit and revise this narrative.

VISIONS B Assessment Program • Copyright © Heinle

VISIONS STUDENT RESOURCE

Persuasive Checklist

Use this checklist to evaluate your own writing and your classmates' writing.

_____ **Interesting title**

_____ **Name**

_____ **Date**

Introduction

1. _____ asks a question

2. _____ answers a question

3. _____ gives 3 supporting reasons for answer

Body

1. _____ begins with "First, . . ."

2. _____ restates reason # 1

3. _____ gives three supporting details/examples

1. _____ begins with "Next, . . ."

2. _____ restates reason # 2

3. _____ gives three supporting details/examples

1. _____ begins with "Finally, . . ."

2. _____ restates reason # 3

3. _____ gives three supporting details/examples

Conclusion

1. _____ begins with "In conclusion . . ."

2. _____ restates introduction answer

3. _____ restates 3 supporting reasons

_____ I used the Editor's Checklist to edit and revise this persuasive writing.

VISIONS B Assessment Program • Copyright © Heinle

Name _____ Date _____

Oral Presentation Evaluation Sheet

Topic or Title _____

Presenter or Group _____

Did the presenter or group:	lowest		mid		highest
1. make use of eye contact and facial expressions?	1	2	3	4	5
2. have a good opening?	1	2	3	4	5
3. change the pitch and tone of voice?	1	2	3	4	5
4. use interesting and specific language?	1	2	3	4	5
5. use pauses or emphasis on key words?	1	2	3	4	5
6. support ideas with details and examples?	1	2	3	4	5
7. use gestures or action?	1	2	3	4	5
8. use visuals?	1	2	3	4	5
9. speak clearly?	1	2	3	4	5
10. have a good closing?	1	2	3	4	5

For a Reader's Theater or play

11. wear costumes or use props?	1	2	3	4	5
12. act so I believed the story?	1	2	3	4	5

Name _____ Date _____

Speaker _____ Topic _____

Active Listening Checklist

Use this checklist to evaluate how well you listen and understand.

1. I liked _____ because _____
   _____

2. I want to know more about _____
   _____

3. I thought the opening was interesting.   ____ Yes ____ No

4. The speaker stayed on the topic.   ____ Yes ____ No

5. I did not understand _____
   _____

6. I needed the speaker to repeat or clarify _____
   _____

7. My own criteria: _____
   _____

8. My own criteria: _____
   _____

9. My own criteria: _____
   _____

VISIONS B Assessment Program • Copyright © Heinle

Speaking Checklist

Use this checklist to evaluate your speaking.

1. Did I speak too slowly, too quickly, or just right? _____

2. Was the tone of my voice too high, too low, or just right? _____

3. Did I speak loudly enough for the audience to hear me?   ____ Yes ____ No

4. Did I produce the correct intonation patterns of sentences? ____ Yes ____ No

5. Did I have a good opening?   ____ Yes ____ No

6. Did I look at my audience?   ____ Yes ____ No

7. Did I speak with feeling?   ____ Yes ____ No

8. Did I support my ideas with facts and examples?   ____ Yes ____ No

9. Did I tell the audience how I feel about the topic?   ____ Yes ____ No

10. Did I use interesting, specific words?   ____ Yes ____ No

11. Did I use visuals to make the speech interesting?   ____ Yes ____ No

My Own Criteria

12. _____   ____ Yes ____ No

13. _____   ____ Yes ____ No

14. _____   ____ Yes ____ No

VISIONS STUDENT RESOURCE

Viewing Checklist

Visuals help you understand texts and presentations better. Analyzing visuals for their usefulness will help you to learn how to create good visuals. Think about these points as you view and create visuals.

1. Do I understand the purpose of this visual? _____ Yes _____ No

2. What is the purpose? _____
_____

3. Does this visual help me to understand better? _____ Yes _____ No

4. How does it help me understand? _____
_____

5. Is the visual labeled clearly? _____ Yes _____ No

6. Does the visual give me extra information? _____ Yes _____ No

7. What did I learn from the visual? _____
_____

8. Would I create the same visual for this text/presentation? _____ Yes _____ No

9. What would I do differently? _____
_____

10. My own viewing criteria: _____
_____

11. My own viewing criteria: _____
_____

VISIONS B Assessment Program • Copyright © Heinle

VISIONS B Assessment Program • Copyright © Heinle

Name _____   Date _____

Word Study and Spelling

Keep a list of new words that you learn. Use a dictionary, a glossary, or the Newbury House Dictionary CD-ROM to find definitions.

Word	Page	Sentence from Reading	Definition	Your Sentence

Name _____

Date _____

Word Study and Spelling Assessment Chart

1. Exchange your *Word Study and Spelling* pages with a partner.
2. Choose five words and ask your partner to spell them on a piece of paper.
3. Choose another five words and ask your partner to write a sentence using each.
4. Check your partner's work.
5. Record the number of words spelled correctly in the first row of your partner's chart.
6. Record the number of words used correctly in a sentence in the second row.
7. Record the words that were spelled or used incorrectly in the third row.

My Score	Unit 1	Unit 2	Unit 3	Unit 4	Unit 5	Unit 6
How many words did I spell correctly?	Correct: Incorrect:	Correct: Incorrect:	Correct: Incorrect:	Correct: Incorrect:	Correct: Incorrect:	Correct: Incorrect:
How many words did I use in a sentence correctly?	Correct: Incorrect:	Correct: Incorrect:	Correct: Incorrect:	Correct: Incorrect:	Correct: Incorrect:	Correct: Incorrect:
Which words do I need to study?						

Name _____

Independent Reading Record

Keep track of your reading here. Share this record with your classmates and talk about readings that you enjoyed.

Date	Title of Reading and Author	Reading Time	Pages Read	Comments
Sept. 2	*The Pearl* by John Steinbeck	20 minutes	pp. 60–85	Could relate to Kino's thoughts and feelings; great ending!

Student Self-Assessment

Part I: Circle the number that best describes you.

How I feel about my work in English:	Unhappy	1	2	3	4	Happy
My speaking and listening are:	Not Improving	1	2	3	4	Improving
My reading is:	Not Improving	1	2	3	4	Improving
My writing is:	Not Improving	1	2	3	4	Improving
My work is:	Too Hard	1	2	3	4	Too Easy
My work is:	Not Interesting	1	2	3	4	Very Interesting

Part II: Complete these sentences.

1. The best thing that I did/learned lately is _____

   _____

2. I would like to learn _____

   _____

3. I am best at _____

   _____

4. I need some help with _____

   _____

5. My learning and practicing plans are to _____

   _____

Activity and Project Reflection

Think about the activities and projects that you have done in class. Then answer these questions.

1. The most interesting activity or project that we did was _____
_____

2. I think this activity or project was interesting because _____
_____
_____
_____
_____

3. In this activity or project, I learned _____
_____
_____
_____
_____

4. Did anyone else work with you or help you with your learning? How did he or she help you? _____
_____
_____
_____
_____

Test-Taking Tips

Use these tips to help you improve your performance on tests.

BEFORE THE TEST

1. Complete all of your assignments on time.

2. Take notes in class as you go over your assignments.

3. Save and review your class notes, assignments, and quizzes.

4. Ask your teacher what topics will be covered on the test.

5. Ask your teacher what kind of test you will take. For example, will the questions be true/false, multiple choice, or essay?

6. Be organized. Make a study guide. Making note cards or rewriting information will help you review.

7. Study, and then get a good night's sleep before the test.

8. Eat a good, healthy breakfast on the day of the test.

9. Bring everything that you need to the test (pencils, erasers, pens, and so on).

DURING THE TEST

1. Pay close attention to the teacher's instructions. Ask questions if you do not understand.

2. Read the instructions on the test carefully.

3. Look at the test before you begin to see how long it is.

4. Don't spend too much time on any one section or question. Skip questions that you don't know. Return to them if you have time at the end.

5. Watch the time to make sure you finish the whole test.

6. Save time to look over the test before you turn it in. Don't worry if other students finish before you. Use all the time that you have.

AFTER THE TEST

1. When your test is returned to you, look at it carefully.

2. Look up the answers to any questions you left blank or got wrong.

3. Ask your teacher about any questions that you still don't understand. The same question might appear again on another test.

VISIONS B Assessment Program • Copyright © Heinle

Test-Taking Tips (cont . . .)

TYPES OF TEST QUESTIONS

TRUE/FALSE STATEMENTS

Decide if the following statement is *true* or *false*.

> _*False*_   **1.** All trees lose their leaves in the winter.

1. Read the statements carefully.

2. Look for anything in the statement that is not true. If any detail is false, then the whole statement is false.

3. Watch out for absolute words like *always, all, never, no, best,* and *worst.* These may be clues that the statement is false.

MULTIPLE-CHOICE QUESTIONS

Choose the correct answer from the list of choices.

> **1.** Which type of tree loses its leaves in the fall?
> **a.** coniferous tree   **b.** pine tree   **c.** deciduous tree   **d.** fir tree

1. Read the question carefully before you look at the answer choices.

2. Answer the question before you look at the choices. Then see if your answer is listed.

3. Read all of the answers before you choose one.

4. If you are not sure which answer is correct, cross out the ones that you know are wrong. Choose one of the answers that is left.

ESSAY QUESTIONS

Write one or more paragraphs to answer the question.s

> **1.** Describe three things that happen to deciduous trees in the fall.

1. Know what you are being asked to do (for example, *describe, discuss, compare, explain,* and so on).

2. Plan your essay before you begin to write. Making a basic outline first will help you stay focused.

3. Include a *thesis statement, supporting evidence,* and a *conclusion.*

4. Show how much you know, but stay focused. Include only information that is relevant to your topic or thesis.

5. Write neatly. Your teacher must be able to read your answer.

Lesson Plan Checklist

for *The Sheltered Instruction Observation Protocol*

I. PREPARATION

_____ Write content objectives clearly for students.

_____ Write language objectives clearly for students.

_____ Choose content concepts appropriate for age and educational background level of students.

_____ Identify supplementary materials to use (graphs, models, visuals).

_____ Adapt content (e.g., text, assignment) to all levels of student proficiency.

_____ Plan meaningful activities that integrate lesson concepts (e.g., surveys, letter writing, simulations, constructing models) with language practice opportunities for reading, writing, listening, and/or speaking.

II. INSTRUCTION

Building Background

_____ Explicitly link concepts to students' backgrounds and experiences.

_____ Explicitly link past learning and new concepts.

_____ Emphasize key vocabulary (e.g., introduce, write, repeat, and highlight for students to see).

Comprehensible Input

_____ Use speech appropriate for students' proficiency level (e.g., slower rate, enunciation, and simple sentence structure for beginners).

_____ Explain academic tasks clearly.

_____ Use a variety of techniques to make content concepts clear (e.g., modeling, visuals, hands-on activities, demonstrations, gestures, body language).

Strategies

_____ Provide ample opportunities for students to use strategies (e.g., problem solving, predicting, organizing, summarizing, categorizing, evaluating, self-monitoring).

_____ Use scaffolding techniques consistently (providing the right amount of support to move students from one level of understanding to a higher level) throughout the lesson.

_____ Use a variety of question types throughout the lesson, including those that promote higher-order thinking skills throughout the lesson (e.g., literal, analytical, and interpretive questions).

Short, D., and Ecchevaria, J. (1999). *The Sheltered Instruction Observation Protocol: A Tool for Teacher-Researcher Collaboration and Professional Development.* Center for Research on Education, Diversity & Excellence, University of California, Santa Cruz.

Lesson Plan Checklist (cont . . .)

for *The Sheltered Instruction Observation Protocol*

Interaction

_____ Provide frequent opportunities for interaction and discussion between teacher/student and among students about lessons and concepts, and encourage elaborated responses.

_____ Use group configurations that support language and content objectives of the lesson.

_____ Consistently provide sufficient wait time for student responses.

_____ Give ample opportunities for students to clarify key concepts in L1 as needed with aide, peer, or L1 text.

Practice/Application

_____ Provide hands-on materials and/or manipulatives for students to practice using new content knowledge.

_____ Provide activities for students to apply content and language knowledge in the classroom.

_____ Use activities that integrate all language skills (reading, writing, listening, and speaking).

Lesson Delivery

_____ Support content objectives clearly.

_____ Support language objectives clearly.

_____ Engage students approximately 90–100% of the period (with most students taking part in and working on task throughout the lesson).

_____ Pace the lesson appropriately to the students' ability level.

Review/Assessment

_____ Give a comprehensive review of key vocabulary.

_____ Give a comprehensive review of key content concepts.

_____ Provide feedback to students regularly on their output (e.g., language, content, work).

_____ Conduct assessments of student comprehension and learning throughout lesson on all lesson objectives (e.g., spot checking, group response) throughout the lesson.

Short, D., and Ecchevaria, J. (1999). *The Sheltered Instruction Observation Protocol: A Tool for Teacher-Researcher Collaboration and Professional Development.* Center for Research on Education, Diversity & Excellence, University of California, Santa Cruz.

VISIONS TEACHER RESOURCE

Rubric for Oral Reading Fluency

adapted from the National Assessment of Educational Progress (NAEP)
Scale for Assessing Oral Reading Fluency

Point Scale	Description of Oral Reading Fluency
4	Reads primarily in large, meaningful phrase groups. Although some regressions, repetitions, and deviations from text may be present, these do not appear to detract from the overall structure of the story. Preservation of the author's syntax is consistent. Some or most of the story is read with expressive interpretation.
3	Reads primarily in three- or four-word phrase groups. Some smaller groupings may be present. However, the majority of phrasing seems appropriate and preserves the syntax of the author. Little or no expressive interpretation is present.
2	Reads primarily in two-word phrases with some three- or four-word groupings. Some word-by-word reading may be present. Word groupings may seem awkward and unrelated to the larger context of the sentence or passage.
1	Reads primarily word by word. Occasional two-word or three-word phrases may occur, but these are infrequent and/or they do not preserve meaningful syntax.

VISIONS B Assessment Program • Copyright © Heinle

Rubric for Oral Presentations

	3 points	2 points	1 point
Presentation	• Student uses appropriate eye contact and facial expressions. • Student uses gestures consistently. • Student seems at ease and engages the audience.	• Student uses some eye contact and facial expressions. • Student makes some use of gestures. • Student begins to overcome timidity and engages the audience.	• Student uses no eye contact. • Student uses no gestures. • Student is remote and isolated from the audience.
Speaking Mechanics	• Student uses exciting pitch and tone of voice. • Student is clear and easily understood. • Student pauses and emphasizes key words.	• Student sometimes varies pitch and tone. • Student is sometimes difficult to hear. • Student uses some pauses and emphasis for key words.	• Student uses no change in pitch or tone. • Student is difficult to hear. • Student uses no pauses or emphasis for key words.
Content	• Opening and closing are good. • Grammar and word choice are easy to understand. • Central idea is supported with details and examples. • The speaker's individuality and perspective are clear.	• Opening and closing are perfunctory. • Grammar and word choice are usually appropriate. • Central idea is not fully developed. • There is some sense of the speaker's individual perspective.	• There is no opening or closing. • Grammar and word choice make the presentation hard to understand. • The central idea is not clear. • There is no sense of the speaker's individual perspective.
Visuals/ Props/ Costumes	• Visuals and props enhance and clarify presentation. • Costumes are appropriate for presentation (Reader's Theater).	• Visuals and props provide limited clarification and enhancement of presentation. • Costumes are somewhat appropriate for presentation (Reader's Theater).	• There are no visuals. • There are no props. • There are no costumes (Reader's Theater).

Name _____ Teacher _____

Grade _____ Semester/Year _____

<table>
<tr><td>RUBRIC</td><td>1. Limited progress</td><td>Little or no progress toward mastery of standard.</td></tr>
<tr><td></td><td>2. Partial progress</td><td>Some progress toward mastery of standard.</td></tr>
<tr><td></td><td>3. Average progress</td><td>Masters the standard for his/her level.</td></tr>
<tr><td></td><td>4. Advanced progress</td><td>Exceeds the standard for his/her level.</td></tr>
</table>

LISTENING AND SPEAKING STANDARDS ASSESSMENT CHECKLIST	Marking Period and Scores			
	1	2	3	4
Listen actively and purposefully				
1. Determine purpose of listening, such as to gain information, to problem solve, to enjoy				
2. Eliminate barriers to effective listening				
3. Understand major ideas while listening				
4. Understand supporting evidence while listening				
5. Listen to take notes				
6. Listen to organize				
7. Listen to summarize				
8. Distinguish and produce sounds				
9. Distinguish and produce intonation patterns				
Total Points	/36	/36	/36	/36
Listen critically to analyze and evaluate a speaker's message				
10. Interpret verbal messages				
11. Interpret nonverbal messages				
12. Interpret purposes				
13. Interpret perspectives				
14. Identify and analyze speaker's persuasive techniques and credibility				
15. Distinguish the speaker's opinion from verifiable fact				
16. Self-monitor understanding of spoken message				
17. Seek clarification as needed				
18. Compare own perception of a message with others' perception				
19. Evaluate spoken message for content				
20. Evaluate spoken message for credibility				
21. Evaluate spoken message for delivery				
Total Points	/48	/48	/48	/48
Listen to enjoy and appreciate spoken language				
22. Listen to fluent readings of classic and contemporary works				
23. Analyze oral interpretations of literature for effects on the listener				
24. Analyze aesthetic language for its effects		'		
Total Points	/12	/12	/12	/12

VISIONS B Assessment Program • Copyright © Heinle

VISIONS TEACHER RESOURCE

LISTENING AND SPEAKING STANDARDS ASSESSMENT CHECKLIST (cont...)	Marking Period and Scores			
	1	2	3	4
Listen and speak to gain knowledge of culture				
25. Connect own information with the experiences of others				
26. Connect own insights with the experiences of others				
27. Connect own ideas with the experiences of others				
28. Compare oral traditions across regions				
29. Compare oral traditions across cultures				
30. Identify how language use, such as labels and sayings, reflects regions				
31. Identify how language use, such as labels and sayings, reflects cultures				
Total Points	/28	/28	/28	/28
Speak clearly and appropriately to different audiences on different occasions				
32. Adapt word choice to audience, purpose, and occasion				
33. Adapt diction to audience, purpose, and occasion				
34. Adapt usage to audience, purpose, and occasion				
35. Demonstrate communication skills—interviewing, reporting, requesting, and providing information				
36. Present dramatic interpretations of experiences				
37. Present dramatic interpretations of stories				
38. Present dramatic interpretations of poems or plays				
39. Generate criteria to evaluate own presentations				
40. Generate criteria to evaluate others' presentations				
41. Use effective rate for the audience and setting				
42. Use effective volume for the audience and setting				
43. Use effective pitch for the audience and setting				
44. Use effective tone for the audience and setting				
45. Clarify spoken ideas with evidence				
46. Clarify spoken ideas with elaboration				
47. Clarify spoken ideas with examples				
48. Support spoken ideas with evidence				
49. Support spoken ideas with elaboration				
50. Support spoken ideas with examples				
51. Employ content area vocabulary in context				
Total Points	/80	/80	/80	/80

Name _____ Teacher _____

Grade _____ Semester/Year _____

READING STANDARDS ASSESSMENT CHECKLIST	Marking Period and Scores			
	1	2	3	4
Use a variety of word recognition and analysis strategies				
1. Apply knowledge of letter-sound correspondences to words				
2. Apply knowledge of language structure to words				
3. Apply knowledge of context to words				
4. Identify prefixes and suffixes				
5. Identify Greek and Latin root words				
6. Locate word meanings, pronunciations, and derivations in dictionaries, glossaries, and other sources				
Total Points	/24	/24	/24	/24
Read with fluency and understanding in texts at appropriate difficulty levels				
7. Read regularly in independent-level and instructional-level materials				
8. Read aloud to reflect understanding of text and engage listeners				
9. Read silently with increasing ease for longer periods				
10. Adjust reading rate for purpose				
Total Points	/16	/16	/16	/16
Read widely for different purposes in varied sources				
11. Read classic and contemporary texts				
12. Read in varied sources, such as plays, novels, newspapers, textbooks, and electronic texts				
13. Read for varied purposes, such as for information, entertainment, and appreciation of craft				
14. Read to take action, such as to complete forms, respond, and make a recommendation				
Total Points	/16	/16	/16	/16
Acquire an extensive vocabulary through reading and systematic word study				
15. Develop vocabulary by listening to selections read aloud				
16. Draw on experiences to interpret words in context, such as figurative language, multiple-meaning words, and analogies				
17. Use multiple reference aids to clarify meaning and usage, such as a thesaurus, a synonym finder, a dictionary, and software				
18. Determine meanings of derivatives by knowledge of root words and affixes				
19. Study word meanings systematically				
20. Distinguish denotative and connotative meanings				
21. Use word origins to understand historical influences on word meanings				
Total Points	/28	/28	/28	/28
Use a variety of strategies to comprehend a wide range of texts of increasing levels of difficulty				
22. Use own knowledge and experience to comprehend texts				
23. Establish and adjust purposes for reading				
24. Monitor own comprehension				
25. Make modifications when understanding breaks down—rereading portions aloud, using reference aids, searching for clues, and asking questions				
26. Describe mental images that texts evoke				

VISIONS B Assessment Program • Copyright © Heinle

VISIONS TEACHER RESOURCE

READING STANDARDS ASSESSMENT CHECKLIST (cont...)	Marking Period and Scores			
	1	2	3	4
27. Use text structure and progression of ideas to locate and recall information				
28. Determine main ideas and supporting details				
29. Paraphrase and summarize text to recall, inform, or organize ideas				
30. Draw inferences, such as conclusions or generalizations				
31. Support inferences with text evidence and experience				
32. Find similarities and differences across texts				
33. Distinguish fact and opinion in various texts				
34. Answer different types and levels of questions—open-ended, literal, interpretive, multiple choice, true/false, and short answer				
35. Represent text information in different ways—outlines, timelines, and graphic organizers				
36. Use strategies to learn important ideas, such as preview, question, reread, and record				
37. Use strategies to recall important ideas, such as preview, question, reread, and record				
Total Points	/64	/64	/64	/64
Express and support responses to various types of texts				
38. Offer observations, make connections, react, speculate, interpret, and raise questions in response to texts				
39. Interpret text ideas through journal writing, discussion, enactment, and media				
40. Support responses by referring to relevant aspects of text and own experiences				
41. Connect, compare, and contrast ideas, themes, and issues across texts				
Total Points	/16	/16	/16	/16
Analyze the characteristics of various types of text (genres)				
42. Identify purposes of different types of text—to inform, entertain, influence, or express				
43. Recognize distinguishing features of genres, including biography, historical fiction, informational text, and poetry				
44. Compare communication in different forms				
45. Understand and identify literary terms				
46. Understand literary forms by recognizing types of text				
47. Understand literary forms by distinguishing among types of text				
48. Analyze characters for traits, motivation, conflicts, points of view, relationships, and changes				
49. Recognize and analyze story plot, setting, and problem resolution				
50. Describe how the author's point of view or perspective affects the text				
51. Analyze ways authors organize and present ideas				
52. Recognize and interpret literary devices—flashback, foreshadowing, and symbolism				
53. Recognize how style, tone, and mood contribute to the effect of a text				
Total Points	/48	/48	/48	/48
Inquire and conduct research using a variety of sources				
54. Form and revise questions for investigations				
55. Use text organizers to locate information—headings, graphics, and tables of contents				
56. Use multiple sources to locate research information—electronic texts, print, and experts				
57. Interpret and use graphic sources of information (maps, charts, timelines, and tables) to address research questions				
58. Summarize and organize information from multiple sources in notes, outlines, or charts				
59. Produce research projects and reports in effective formats for various audiences				
60. Draw conclusions from information gathered from multiple sources				
61. Use compiled information and knowledge to raise additional questions				
62. Present organized statements, reports, and speeches using visuals				
Total Points	/36	/36	/36	/36
Read to increase knowledge of own culture, the culture of others, and the common elements of cultures				
63. Compare text events with own experiences and other readers' experiences				
64. Determine distinctive and common characteristics of cultures				
65. Articulate and discuss themes and connections that cross cultures				
Total Points	/12	/12	/12	/12

Name _____   Teacher _____

Grade _____   Semester/Year _____

RUBRIC	1. Limited progress	Little or no progress toward mastery of standard.
	2. Partial progress	Some progress toward mastery of standard.
	3. Average progress	Masters the standard for his/her level.
	4. Advanced progress	Exceeds the standard for his/her level.

WRITING STANDARDS ASSESSMENT CHECKLIST	Marking Period and Scores			
	1	2	3	4
Write for a variety of purposes and audiences and in a variety of forms				
1. Write to express				
2. Write to discover				
3. Write to record				
4. Write to develop				
5. Write to reflect on ideas				
6. Write to problem solve				
7. Write to influence—persuade, request, and argue				
8. Write to inform—explain, narrate, describe, and report				
9. Write to entertain—humorous poems or short stories				
10. Select and use voice and style appropriate to audience				
11. Select and use voice and style appropriate to purpose				
12. Choose appropriate form for purpose—journal, letter, editorial, review, poem, memoir, narrative, and instructional text				
13. Use literary devices effectively—suspense, dialogue, and figurative language				
14. Produce cohesive and coherent texts by organizing ideas				
15. Produce cohesive and coherent texts by using effective transitions				
16. Produce cohesive and coherent texts by choosing precise wording				
Total Points	/64	/64	/64	/64
Compose original texts applying the conventions of written language, such as capitalization, punctuation, penmanship, and spelling, to communicate clearly				
17. Write legibly, using cursive or manuscript as appropriate				
18. Capitalize correctly to clarify and enhance meaning				
19. Punctuate correctly to clarify and enhance meaning				
20. Spell: open and closed syllables, consonant before -le, syllable boundary patterns				
21. Write with accurate spelling of roots, inflections, suffixes, and prefixes				
22. Spell derivatives correctly by applying the spelling of bases				
23. Spell derivatives correctly by applying the spelling of affixes				
24. Spell frequently misspelled words, such as *their, they're, there*				
25. Use resources to find correct spellings				
26. Spell accurately in final drafts				
27. Understand the influence of languages and cultures on spelling				
Total Points	/44	/44	/44	/44
Apply standard grammar and usage to communicate clearly and effectively in writing				
28. Use regular and irregular plurals correctly				
29. Write varying sentence types—compound and complex				
30. Write correctly punctuated independent and dependent clauses				
31. Use conjunctions to connect ideas				
32. Use subject-verb agreement				
33. Use pronoun referents				
34. Use parts of speech				
35. Use adjectives—regular, comparative, and superlative				

VISIONS B Assessment Program • Copyright © Heinle

VISIONS TEACHER RESOURCE